OTHER
Harlequin Romances

by REBECCA STRATTON

ISLE OF
THE GOLDEN DRUM

by

REBECCA STRATTON

Harlequin Books

TORONTO • LONDON • NEW YORK • AMSTERDAM • SYDNEY • WINNIPEG

Original hardcover edition published in 1975
by Mills & Boon Limited

ISBN 0-373-01991-2

Harlequin edition published July 1976

CHAPTER ONE

CARYS had never felt so frightened in her life before and she kept her eyes tight shut, not only in anticipation of the inevitable crash, but also in a silent prayer that they would not be drowned in the vast expanse of the Pacific Ocean that was waiting down there below them. She had flown with Mike and his father before in the big executive aircraft, but always the flight had been without incident, the prospect of crashing into the sea had never even entered her head —now it was about to become a terrifying reality.

This flight, as the previous ones had been, had promised to be uneventful, although Carys had been rather more preoccupied with her own affairs than usual because it was not every day that a girl received a proposal of marriage from her employer's son and heir.

Carys had been in Karl Shushter's employ for six months, and in that time she had come to the conclusion that, while she liked his son Michael quite a lot, the man himself left much to be desired, both as an employer and as a man. He boasted of being a hard-headed businessman, a firm believer in the adage that every man, and woman, has their price, and it was a conviction that Carys was finding increasingly hard to stomach.

Yesterday she had finally made up her mind that she was ready to sacrifice what was undeniably a well-paid post and return to England. Enough was enough and she had suffered Karl Shushter's cut-throat methods to the point of revolt. With the decision settled in her own mind it had come like a bolt out of the blue when last night Mike had suddenly asked her to marry him, and she had refused him out of hand without even stopping to consider what an opportunity it might be for her.

She liked Mike well enough, he was charming and lighthearted, an attentive escort and lots of fun to be with, but she suspected that in time he could absorb some of his father's less endearing qualities. While they had been in Honolulu Mike had wined and dined her, taken her to all the best night spots in the city and of course flirted with her.

Not that she took his flirting seriously, for a girl with her looks came in for more than her share of attention. Long dark hair and wide grey eyes in a heart-shaped face, and a slim rounded figure, brought her the attention of any number of men, but Mike had jealously guarded her from any who came too close. For all that his proposal had come as a complete surprise, for she had thought him no more serious about their relationship than she was herself.

He had been taken aback but not deterred by her refusal, and she knew he would try again when he considered that the moment was right. Mike, like his father, was used to having what he had set his mind on having, and he would not give up. Although so far unmarried himself, he was no stranger to the ups and downs of marriage and divorce, for his father, during Mike's twenty-four years, had given him two stepmothers, both of whom had divorced him.

Carys knew, too, that if Karl Shushter knew of her refusal to marry his son he would quite probably take the initiative from her in the matter of her leaving his employ. He doted on Mike as the only child of three marriages, and the idea of a mere secretary, and an English one at that, having the temerity to turn down his son would strike him as ample grounds for dismissal.

Both Mike and his father were qualified pilots and they almost always flew the big plane themselves because they enjoyed the challenge of flying, and it was Mike who now fought to bring the aircraft down as smoothly as possible while its engines sputtered and whined and finally died altogether as they came down even closer to the surface of the sea.

It was Karl Shushter, cursing angrily, who found that their radio was not operating properly and that their repeated and frantic 'mayday' calls went unheard. If he ever got out of the situation alive, Karl Shushter swore tight-lipped, somebody would pay for that dud radio with his job. It did not yet occur to him that it had been working when they left Honolulu.

Her head buried in a cushion resting on her knees, Carys put all her hopes in a tiny speck of island that they had spotted below them only minutes before, and prayed that if it was inhabited the inhabitants would witness their disaster and inform someone who could help.

When the engines at last cut out altogether the air

7

outside whined shrilly as they came down, and she could hear Mike cursing as he fought to steady the plane and bring it down as level as possible, hoping to keep it afloat at least long enough for them to get free.

The impact came suddenly and almost unexpectedly after a whole gamut of sensations that spun in kaleidoscope fashion through her brain before the actual shock of hitting the water—after that there was nothing for quite a while.

Next impressions were hazy, like something happening at a distance, and Carys felt herself dragged from the plane, only half aware of what was going on. She felt wet but not cold and the sensation of being rocked was quite pleasant despite the raging ache in her head. It was some time before she realised that they must be in a boat, and that the firm softness that supported her head was Mike's arm as he held her on his lap.

She stirred, frowning at the brightness of the sunshine when she opened her eyes, and immediately closed them again because it made her head ache even more. A hand touched her cheek, lightly tapping, trying to bring her round. 'Carys? Honey?' Mike's anxious voice penetrated the haze in her brain, and once more she opened her eyes.

His good-looking features looked down at her anxiously, his face and hair shiningly wet like the shirt that clung to his body, and he ran his fingers through the damp fringe across his forehead as she looked up at him. They were in a boat, a small boat of some kind that rocked on the gentle swell and almost lulled her back into unconsciousness again.

The sky was a bright, clear blue only lightly dotted with tiny white clouds and she gazed up at it for several seconds before she tried to focus her eyes on Mike again. 'We've—we've been rescued?' she guessed, and found her lips sticky with salt water and her throat huskily dry when she tried to speak.

'We've been rescued,' Mike agreed with a relieved grin. 'I guess we're luckier than we deserve to be—we came down right close to that island we saw.'

'Oh!'

She looked down at herself and saw that the softly flared dress she had started out in was now little more than a limp wet swathe of material that clung to her shape, moulded revealingly to every curve and exposing most of her slim legs. Her feet were bare, her shoes apparently lost in the crash, and her long hair stuck to her neck and shoulders with the stickiness of salt water. She struggled upright, trying to sit instead of lying across Mike's lap, and the rocking of the boat increased alarmingly with her movements.

'Hey! Sit still and take it easy!' The voice came from further along the boat and she turned startled eyes to the stranger in their midst.

He partially hid her view of Karl Shushter who was huddled morosely in the stern, his broad shoulders hunched and his head between his hands, soaking wet and looking much more vulnerable than Carys would have believed possible. In the centre of the frail craft, wielding a pair of oars with an ease that was deceptive, sat their rescuer, and Carys looked looked at him for a moment with vague, curious eyes.

He was tanned to a deep golden brown, that much registered immediately, and the fact that he had light blond hair showed up the fact even more starkly. Another inescapable feature that contrasted strongly with the colour of his sun-browned skin was the eyes that watched her briefly until she settled down in the bottom of the boat and it steadied again. They were a bright, light blue, narrowed against the brightness of the sun and creased at their corners as if he smiled a lot, although he was not smiling now but looked vaguely annoyed, as if he came to their rescue only reluctantly.

'I'm sorry,' she said huskily, but her apology was ignored as he bent on the oars again, pulling the light boat with its overload of passengers through the deep blue water.

'Are you feeling better?' Mike asked, and put an arm around her shoulders—a gesture that, oddly enough, struck Carys as possessive rather than comforting, and she noticed the swift elevation of their rescuer's light brows, although he appeared not to be looking at them.

'I feel all right,' she said uncertainly. 'But my head aches.'

'Poor sweetheart!' Mike put a hand to her throbbing head and smiled down at her encouragingly. 'You banged your head when we hit the water, I guess, we'll take a look at it when we get ashore.'

The bottom of the boat scraped on sand suddenly and then tipped slightly when the water was drawn back by the tide. The man at the oars leapt nimbly out into the shallow surf and held the bow while

Karl Shushter climbed over the side, then Mike followed and together they pulled the boat on to the sand, high and dry.

Reaching into the boat for her, Mike tried to lift her out, but her own legs were quite incredibly weak and Mike must have been more affected than he appeared at first, for he failed to lift her clear and she grabbed hastily at the side, only just saving herself from falling backwards. Brushing Mike firmly aside, their rescuer reached over and hauled her clear in one easy movement, heedless of her cry of surprise or Mike's frown.

'I could have done that!' Mike objected, but he might not have spoken for all the notice the stranger took of him. He set Carys on her feet briefly, then slipped a hand under her legs and lifted her into his arms.

'You'd better get your own strength back before you try lifting anyone else,' he advised Mike. 'Can you make it to the house O.K.?'

Mike merely nodded, his frown well in evidence as he turned and looked at his father. 'We're O.K.,' he said shortly. 'Carys hit her head when we landed, that's why she's a little muzzy.' He looked up from the long sandy beach at the house set back among trees, and raised a brow enquiringly. 'Is there a doctor on this godforsaken island?'

Carys instinctively put an arm around the stranger's neck, feeling quite alarmingly weak and woolly-headed still and content to allow herself to be carried because she did not think she could have walked, even had she been given the opportunity. Far from describing the island as godforsaken, from what she could see of it so far it was closer to paradise than anything she had ever seen before, and she even felt a slight tingle of excitement at the prospect of being on a desert island. Maybe they were marooned there for hours anyway, if not for several days, but she was so thankful to see solid earth again that she would have been happy to be anywhere.

The land curved inward where they came ashore, forming a natural bay, with white sand stretching round as far as a thick growth of trees one side and what appeared to be sheer rock cliffs the other. The beach sloped up from the water's edge and was backed by more trees, almost a forest of them as far as she could see, and in their shelter stood the house their rescuer had referred to.

A large white house, set just far enough forward from the sheltering trees to catch the sun and yet still be cool, and with what must be a perfect view of the bay and the beach. Single-storied, it had a green roof and a verandah that ran the whole width of its front-age and supported a mass of vines that she recognised as the ubiquitous bougainvillea, its purple blossoms almost completely hiding the front of the building.

'It's beautiful!' Her exclamation was instinctive and the man looked down at her for a second, a hint of smile on his mouth and glinting in those light blue eyes.

'I like it,' he said, 'though it looks like being a little crowded now, and that I don't like so much!'

'Oh! I'm sorry!' She tried not to look at him be-cause the strength of his arms as he carried her gave her a curious sense of intimacy, fostered by the strong, tanned features only inches above her own. She did not even know his name, only that he did not welcome their arrival and made no secret of it.

Mike, catching her murmured apology, frowned impatiently. 'For Pete's sake, honey,' he told her shortly, 'we didn't choose to land on this speck in the ocean! For myself I can't wait to get off it again, but you need a doctor first and some rest, then we'll see about moving out of here somehow or other.'

'I presume you have a radio?' Even coatless and with his clothes torn and clinging damply to him, Karl Shushter gave the impression that he had only to speak for things to happen, but the stranger was shaking his head.

'No, on both counts,' he said quietly, and apparently unperturbed. 'There's no doctor and I have no radio. I prefer it that way.'

'God almighty!' Karl Shushter looked scandalised and, for the moment, bereft of words.

The doors of the house were wide open and it became cool suddenly as they walked into a big shady room, their footsteps deadened by straw matting on the floor. Carys was carried across and set with infinite care on a long and rather battered chaise-longue, then he turned to Mike and his father and indicated chairs.

'I won't be a minute,' he said, as they rather hesitantly sat down, and disappeared for several seconds during which no one said anything, but sat and looked stunned, as if it was not yet believable.

He returned after only a few seconds, so that it was

obvious everything had been ready, bearing a tray on which was a coffee pot and an assortment of pot mugs, with sugar and milk in pottery bowls. He poured some and handed it to Carys, black and strong as it came from the pot, and she assumed it was meant as a treatment for shock, so she took it obediently.

'You've got to be kidding!' Mike said, shaken into speech at last. He looked around him at the big shady room furnished with a minimum of furniture, all of it in a kind of old-fashioned basket weave with lots of big, soft-looking print cushions. There was a big dark oak desk on the other side of the room by an open window, and the whole place looked comfortable and lived-in, though not exactly luxurious, and his opinion of it showed on Mike's good-looking face as he took it all in. 'Where in hell is this, anyway?' he demanded.

Their unwilling host looked at him for a moment as if he considered remarking on his bad manners, but instead he shrugged, his bright blue eyes narrowed as he poured them coffee. He was a big man physically, but it was something in his personality that dominated the big room for all its size and the presence of three other people, and Carys's spine tingled with the hint of challenge in the atmosphere. It seemed possible that even Karl Shushter might meet his match in this man and the thought was surprisingly pleasant to anticipate.

'Its old name is Isleta del Tambor Dorado,' he said quietly, and his blue eyes glittered maliciously when he caught Mike's puzzled frown. 'The Isle of the Golden Drum,' he translated obligingly. 'It's my own personal paradise, or it was until now.' He glanced briefly down at Carys. 'I guess now it's going to be kind of crowded, like I said.'

'You really don't have a radio?' Karl Shushter looked as if he could not believe such primitive conditions existed, much less that he had been landed right in the middle of them. 'Then how do we contact the outside world and let them know where we are?' he demanded.

Their host shrugged his broad shoulders and ran a casual hand through a thick sun-bleached fall of hair that covered half his forehead. 'There's no way,' he informed him quietly. 'No one will call here for another two months when the boat comes with more supplies, until then—you just sit tight, I guess.'

'Like hell we do!' Karl Shushter scowled at him fiercely, a frown that had cowed many men in the past but which seemed to leave the stranger completely unawed. 'You better do something about getting us off this damned island, mister, and quick! I'll make it worth your while, don't worry about that!'

'Believe me, I'd get you off right this minute if it was possible,' the blond man told him bluntly, 'but it's simply not on—like I said, nobody will come near this place for another two months.'

'And yours is the only place here?'

'That's right—that's why I bought it.' The man's blue eyes watched him, almost amused by his obvious frustration and anger. 'You just don't have a choice— you sit tight, till the boat comes.'

'But that's crazy!' It was probably the first time that Karl Shushter had been so calmly informed that he could not buy his way out of a situation, and it made him visibly uneasy, a fact that Carys noted with some satisfaction. 'Do you know who I am, feller?' he demanded, and their host smiled slowly, his eyes crinkling at their corners in a way that fascinated Carys as she watched him surreptitiously from her place on the chaise-longue.

'Sure!' He crossed over to a cabinet and opened the front of it. Taking out a bottle of whisky, he held it out invitingly, and raised a questioning brow. Both Mike and his father shook their heads impatiently, but he poured himself one and turned, casually and with no sign of urgency, leaning back against the cabinet and watching them across the room as he sipped his drink, his eyes still narrowed and revealing a hint of amusement. 'I get to see a newspaper once in a while,' he said in the same quiet and controlled voice, 'and I've seen pictures of both you and your son, Mr. Shushter.' Briefly again the blue eyes switched to Carys, curious and speculative. 'I don't recognise the young lady, though.'

Ignoring the invitation to introduce her, Karl Shushter walked over to him and stood with his hands on his hips, his jaw thrust out, truculent and confident that eventually some form of co-operation would be forthcoming if he offered sufficient incentive. 'Then you know I could pay you anything you ask to get us off this island,' he said. 'You drive a hard bargain, but you name your price, Mr.——?'

'Campbell,' their host supplied quietly, and offered no resentment of the bribe. 'Driff Campbell.'

Karl Shushter frowned briefly, as if the name struck

a chord somewhere, but he had other things in mind and he wasted no time trying to identify the man, only in trying to influence him. 'You know I can buy up a dozen islands like this, so just you think about it, Campbell,' he said, and looked around at the comfortable but shabby room. 'I guess nobody's too proud to make another dollar these days!'

The implication was obvious and Carys felt her stomach curl with embarrassment. Driffort Campbell might not be in the same multi-millionaire class as the Shushters, but he was quite wealthy enough in his own right to remain unmoved by any offer they might make, especially if he was the man he was reputed to be.

He was a writer of full-blooded adventure novels, and his name was familiar to Carys, as it was to several million people around the world, and she could well imagine that the offer of a bribe to let them leave his island hideaway was every bit as pointless as he insisted it was. He would doubtless be only too glad to be rid of them, as he had pointed out.

His gaze dwelt once more on Carys, a scrutiny that gave her a curiously lightheaded feeling, although the sensation was not entirely divorced from the effects of the crash, she recognised that. She was not yet recovered, as she discovered when she got to her feet, for she swayed and would probably have fallen back on to the chaise-longue if Driff Campbell had not been alert to the possibility.

He crossed the room in swift, easy strides and put a steadying arm about her waist when she swayed, his blue eyes narrowed questioningly as he looked down at her. 'Are you all right?' he asked, and she nodded. 'I'll get Luan to find you a place to rest for a while till we sort things out.' She smiled her thanks, looking down a second later at the large hand he extended, his mouth twitching into a faint smile that crinkled his eyes again. 'I guess you'll have to introduce yourself,' he told her.

She put her hand into the strong clasp and he curled his fingers over it. 'I'm Mr. Shushter's secretary, Mr. Campbell,' she told him in a small husky voice. 'Carys Lane.'

'Carys?' He echoed her Celtic name and cocked a curious brow at her. 'Is that English?'

She shook her head, glancing uneasily at Mike as she answered him and noting his frown of dislike. 'It's Welsh,' she said smiling a little uncertainly. 'I'm half Welsh.'

'It's pretty!' The eyes crinkled again and he put a hand under her arm instead of around her waist, as if he too was aware of Mike's frown as he watched them, and wondered if being Karl Shushter's secretary was her only occupation. 'Come on,' he said, 'we'll go find Luan, she'll take care of you.'

She was given little opportunity to say anything to either Mike or his father before she was guided across the big room and out into a narrow passageway that seemed to be at the centre of the house and off which opened several more doors. 'Luan!' He yelled the name at the top of his voice, and almost immediately a tall, slim dark girl came out from one of the other rooms, her dark eyes wide and curious when she looked at Carys.

She could have been no more than eighteen or nineteen and she was pretty in the doll-like fashion that Carys had noticed in Hawaiian girls during her time there, so that she wondered if the girl came from the islands originally. She was golden-skinned rather than brown and her eyes had a slight oriental tilt at their corners that was attractive as well as intriguing. Her accent, however, was mostly American and she wore a simple but quite smart little cotton dress that emphasised her youthfully thin figure.

'Yes, Mr. Campbell?' She smiled with her eyes rather than her mouth and Carys wondered a little dizzily just who and what she was in Driff Campbell's island paradise.

'I'm afraid we have visitors, Luan,' he told her, making no bones about his reluctance to have them there. 'Find John and tell him to see what he can fix in the way of accommodation, will you?'

'He went out in the boat,' Luan told him. 'He went to see if he could salvage anything from the wreck, Mr. Campbell. There might be something floating around he could rescue.'

'I just hope he isn't risking his fool neck for nothing,' Driff Campbell remarked. 'He'll get little thanks if he comes back with bits and pieces that Karl Shushter could buy a thousand times over!'

Luan's dark eyes flicked briefly and curiously in Carys's direction, then she shook her head. 'He won't take chances, not unless he thinks it's worthwhile,' she assured him. 'You know John!'

Driff Campbell passed no opinion, but shrugged his shoulders. 'You let Miss Lane rest awhile,' he told her.

'She's still woozy from a bang on the head and she needs to lie down for a bit.' The girl nodded, taking Carys's arm, and Driff smiled crookedly at her as he turned away. 'You just take it easy for a while, Miss Lane, we'll sort out some sleeping arrangements.'

'Sleeping arrangements?' Carys blinked at him uncertainly as he turned back to her, realising for the first time that they really were going to have to stay on the island for some time. She suddenly felt very small and alone and not a little scared as she looked at her unwilling host.

The bright blue eyes narrowed slightly, but they showed as much amusement as anything else and after a moment she began to feel not only uncomfortably gauche, but also a little angry because he seemed to be laughing at her. 'Did you figure on me turning you out to sleep on the beach?' he asked, and laughed shortly, revealing strong even teeth in the tanned features. 'I admit I don't want you here,' he told her frankly. 'Not you in particular but anybody at all—I work better alone and without interruption, and from what I've seen of your boss and his boy I guess I'm not going to get much peace and quiet from here on, but I'll see you all sleep as comfortably as I can make it for you, O.K.?'

'Thank you, Mr. Campbell.'

He grinned at her amiably. 'You recognised me,' he said. 'I guess your boss didn't, since he seems to think I'm in need of a handout!' He laughed and shook his head, his blue eyes glittering with malicious amusement. 'Maybe you can get it into his head that his room—anybody's room—would be far preferable to his company! Now you go with Luan, Miss Lane, and rest that head—Luan will get you anything you need for your bumps and bruises.'

'Thank you!'

She watched the tall figure stride away, strangely intrigued without quite knowing why, then she turned to the waiting girl and smiled, and Luan took her arm again. 'I'll give you something for your head,' she said. 'Come this way, honey!'

The room she took Carys into seemed to be her own, for it showed every sign of feminine occupation and Luan seemed quite at home there. There was a big double bed over near the window where it would catch the cool breeze off the sea and for a moment Carys wondered if the absent John that Driff Campbell had mentioned was the man who shared Luan's room or if it was their host himself.

There were signs that she shared with someone and the tone of his books suggested that Driff Campbell was no stranger to women. There had been that appreciative glint in Luan's almond eyes when she answered his call too, though perhaps at the moment it would be more fair to let the truth reveal itself rather than jump to conclusions. He had, after all, been very considerate for her welfare, which was more than her employer had been, so she should give him the benefit of the doubt.

Masculine voices woke Carys from her sleep and she sat up quickly, an impulsive move that she regretted a moment later because her head still felt rather painful. Apart from an aching head, however, she felt remarkably well considering all things, and definitely better for having slept a while, but she was curious to know how Mike and his father were faring with their reluctant host.

Swinging her feet off the bed, she walked, shoeless, to the door on the rug-scattered floor. She was not yet resigned to spending a couple of months on this paradise island, but if it came to it she would probably have to go barefoot the whole time unless the absent John managed to salvage some shoes for her. From what she had noticed of Luan her feet must be several sizes larger than her own, so borrowing was out of the question.

She opened the bedroom door and drew in a sharp breath as she stepped back hastily, for she found herself face to face with a tall, dark-eyed man who looked as if he belonged on a sunny island in the Pacific by right of birth. He had smooth handsome features cast in the mould of what she had come to recognise in several months in Hawaii as pure Polynesian, unlike Luan, who showed a definite trace of the Orient in her almond eyes.

The man smiled and shook his head. 'You timed that well, ma'am,' he told her in the curious blend of accents that was also recognisable as Hawaiian American. 'I came to ask you if you felt like having something to eat now—the others are ready for a meal and we figured you'd better have something too if you felt like it. You feeling better?'

He had an easy, friendly manner and Carys smiled. 'Much better, thank you,' she told him, and looked at him curiously, encouraged by his manner. 'You'll be

John,' she guessed, and her guide smiled as he led the way back to the big room.

'That's right,' he said. 'John Kanaka. You met my wife earlier—Luan.'

'She looked after me,' Carys told him. 'I think I've been sleeping in her—in your room, haven't I?'

'That's right, ma'am, but we've got it all sorted out now,' John Kanaka told her with a grin that suggested it had not been easy. 'You're to have the spare room and Mr. Karl Shushter has the chaise-longue—the young Mr. Shushter has the choice of a hammock or the sun-lounger from the porch.'

'Oh, I see.' Carys could imagine that being delegated to sleeping on the chaise-longue had been very unpopular with Karl Shushter, and Mike would not take kindly to either the idea of a hammock or the sun-lounger. Accustomed to being given the best of everything as a matter of course, they would see it as their host's duty to suffer the inconvenience of a makeshift bed. Either that or they would expect him to find some temporary accommodation for his servants on the verandah. 'I hope we're not going to be too much trouble,' she ventured, and John Kanaka grinned at her over his shoulder as he led the way into the long shady room.

'*You* won't be, ma'am,' he said, his dark eyes gleaming wickedly. 'I can't say for sure 'bout the two men yet, but either way I guess Mr. Campbell can handle it!'

As she followed him into the room, Carys had no doubt at all that Mr. Campbell could handle whatever problems arose, and once more she speculated on a possible clash of wills between her employer and a man who had so far proved more than a match for him. There were quite a few possibilities that could make a two-months' stay on the island quite intriguing, and for a moment she quite looked forward to it.

CHAPTER TWO

MIKE somehow looked curiously alien in their present environment, Carys decided as she stood beside him on the verandah the next morning. It had nothing to do with the informality of his dress, she was used to seeing him in casual clothes, it was more to do with the fact that he did not fit into the character of his surroundings.

On the fashionable beaches of Honolulu in elegantly casual slacks and colourful Hawaiian shirts he had looked perfectly at ease with his background, but here, where there was a certain element of primitiveness about their surroundings, he appeared uneasily out of his depth.

Neither of them looked as elegant as when they left Honolulu yesterday afternoon, but they were, miraculously, alive, and that was all that mattered to Carys. The fact that her once lovely blue dress was now little more than a rag was a minor worry when she considered what could have happened, although the dress she had borrowed from Luan fitted a little too closely and she was conscious of her bare feet.

Her two companions had fared no better and, while Luan had done her best with their clothes in the short time at her disposal, they both looked very much like shipwrecked castaways. Mike's expensive linen suit had not taken kindly to a salt water soaking and he had refused to borrow anything of their host's.

His trousers were clean and freshly laundered, but only a rough copy of their former selves, like his silk shirt, now sadly limp and dull. He wore no jacket and his brown hair looked as if he had done little to it after a night's sleep.

Carys had slept well in the little room that Luan called the guest room. Mike had opted for the comparative comfort of the sun-lounger, brought in from the verandah for the purpose, and it looked comfortable enough to Carys, but Mike insisted that it was like sleeping on a pile of rocks.

Perched on the rail of the verandah he swung one foot, his good-looking face showing a hint of sulkiness that was new to Carys, probably because circumstances had never been quite so against him before.

'You can't expect Hilton standards on a little island like this, Mike,' she told him, and he pulled a face, distorting his good looks grotesquely.

'I don't,' he denied plaintively, 'but I don't expect to have to stand under a cold waterfall to take a bath either! Good grief, this guy Campbell's living in the Stone Age!'

Carys looked at him curiously. It was true that the plumbing, or lack of it, was primitive, for it consisted of a very old and simple pump at the back of the house, and any hot water had to be heated in huge kettles on the kitchen stove. So much Luan had told her last night when she brought her a huge jugful to wash in. The existence of a bathroom had not until now occurred to her.

'Is that what we do for a bath?' she asked, and Mike nodded disgustedly.

'Would you believe it?' he demanded. 'I asked about taking a bath and he told me I'd better just strip off and plunge in, like he does! He's not civilised! No bath, and a bed like a heap of rocks!'

Carys looked vaguely uneasy. In such surroundings she would like to think that she had something more hopeful to look forward to than two months of listening to the Shushters complain about their discomforts. 'I—I suppose you could exchange with me,' she ventured. 'You could have the bedroom and I'll sleep out here on the sun-bed—or maybe we could all three take turn about.'

Mike frowned, but he looked as if he considered it as a possibility. 'I guess we could take turn about,' he agreed. 'At least then we'd all have a decent night's sleep sometimes.'

Carys found it hard to be either pessimistic or downhearted for very long, for there was something about the atmosphere of the island that appealed to her. The purple blossoms that smothered the verandah were headily scented in the morning sunshine, and she bent her face to their cool heads.

The trees to the right of the house were, in fact, no more than a border and beyond them was yellow rock, covered in a variety of scrub and flowers. There was a faint sound of falling water somewhere in the background too, just audible above the swish of the surf, and the thought of being stranded on such a paradise isle intrigued her more at the moment than any thought of getting away.

Isle of the Golden Drum, Driff Campbell had called it, and the name intrigued her. The old name for it was Spanish, unless her scant knowledge of languages had misled her, and she wondered if their host could tell her how the island came to be called Isleta del Tambor Dorado. Or on second thoughts if she could summon enough nerve to ask him.

'It's rather romantic being stranded on a lovely tropical island like this,' she said. 'I wouldn't mind spending the rest of my life here.'

Mike looked at her and frowned discouragingly. 'Well, don't get any ideas about it, honey,' he told her. 'Pop'll expect you to come up with something to get us away from here, not talk about settling here for life!'

'Me?' She looked startled. 'But what on earth can I do?'

Mike played with her thick silky hair for a moment, not looking at her directly. 'He might just suspect that our moronic host has a power boat hidden away some place,' he suggested, and flicked a suggestive brow at her. 'You're a beautiful girl, Carys honey.'

Carys stared at him. 'And you expect me to—to turn on the charm and—oh, for heaven's sake, Mike! He doesn't want us here, he's made that quite plain enough—and he's not moronic, he's a very clever man!'

'Clever?' He frowned, his fingers stilled suddenly. 'How do you figure that out?'

'Driffort Campbell,' she said, 'the writer. He's very well known, Mike, and he certainly isn't as hard up as your father seems to think!'

Mike dismissed his father's lack of tact with a shrug. The bribes usually worked and he evidently considered that Driff Campbell was no different from the rest. 'The name struck a note somewhere,' he admitted, 'but I'm no bookworm, honey. Anyway, being a writer doesn't automatically make him one of the world's rich—rather the reverse, I'd have thought. Aren't they supposed to starve in garrets or something?'

Carys smiled and shook her head. 'Not writers like Driffort Campbell,' she told him. 'He's very unlikely to be holding out for a bigger bribe and I'm sure he'd help us leave if he could! It's obvious he could work a lot better without the company of a host of strangers in his home.'

Mike leaned across and kissed her, slowly and lingeringly beside her mouth. 'Then he'd better do something about getting us rescued, hadn't he?' he suggested. He put his arms around her and drew her to him, smiling down at her. 'I don't mind in the least being stranded on a tropical island with you, my lovely,' he told her in a low voice, 'but I can't see Pop getting enthusiastic about the idea. The sooner we're away from here the sooner I can woo you in the manner to which you're accustomed, too.'

'Mike——'

'You could do worse, you know, honey,' he interrupted. Brushing back the long hair from her forehead, he kissed her and smiled, a slow warm smile. 'You're almost twenty-four and it's high time you were married—preferably to me, the apple of Pop's eye.'

Carys traced the outline of his shirt collar with her forefinger. 'I don't think your father would take kindly to the idea of you making his secretary his daughter-in-law,' she said, but Mike laughed, his confidence unshaken, and drew her closer, pressing his mouth firmly over hers.

There was nothing earth-shattering about Mike's kiss, but it was a pleasant enough experience and she raised no real objection, but nor did she actively encourage it. 'Miss Lane!' She turned her head swiftly when the familiar harsh voice made her step back hastily as if she had been stung.

Karl Shuster looked strangely out of his element, but despite his creased clothes and a shirt borrowed from his host, he still looked the cold and ruthless businessman, and Carys eyed him warily. He was obviously aware that Mike had been taking her out, but she doubted if he realised how the relationship had progressed, or that Mike had proposed to her.

'Can you spare me a minute of your time?' Karl Shushter asked, in such a way that his sarcasm brought a flush of resentment to her cheeks.

She gave Mike a gentle push and stepped away from him, looking at the older man with her dislike of him much more evident than she usually allowed herself to show. 'Of course, Mr. Shushter,' she said.

'What's to be done about getting us off this damned island?' he demanded, and Carys shook her head.

'I don't know,' she told him quietly. 'Mr. Campbell has no radio and no other form of transport than the rowing boat he picked us up in—I don't quite see what we can do about it.'

'You believe this guy when he says that rowboat's all he's got?' he demanded, and Carys nodded.

'Yes, I do,' she told him. 'I have no reason to suppose he's lying about it—he has no reason to.'

'You think not?' He scowled as if he doubted it, and Carys sighed inwardly at the prospect of trying to persuade him it was the truth.

'I'm sure of it, Mr. Shushter,' she said. 'Mr. Campbell lives here alone because it suits him to, he can work when it's quiet and peaceful—we're simply a nuisance to him and he'd be only too glad to help us get away.' She looked at him curiously for a moment. 'Surely there'll be a search for us, won't there?' she asked. 'You were expected in San Diego last night. Somebody's bound to raise the alarm when you don't arrive.'

'I wasn't expected!' Karl Shushter's broad face was flushed and his eyes evaded her disbelieving frown. 'I stopped you phoning Lieberman in San Diego because I didn't want anybody to know I was coming,' he told her. 'I wanted to catch them on the hop—see what they were up to while I was away. Nobody, but nobody, knows we left for San Diego yesterday, Miss Lane, except the guys who cleared us out of Honolulu.'

Carys stared at him for a moment, then she shook her head. 'The—the people in the Honolulu office,' she said in a small husky voice. 'They know where you were going, surely?'

'And have somebody ring San Diego and warn them?' Karl Shushter snapped. 'As far as they know we've gone over to the big island for a short vacation.'

'I see.' It was almost too much, the temptation to suggest that it served him right that he was stranded, but somehow Carys managed it. She looked at his angry features and wondered why it was that she felt a twinge of pity for him suddenly. He was even more at the mercy of circumstances than she had realised. 'They'll discover it sooner or later,' she told him after a moment or two. 'Then they'll organise a search.'

'Who'll know where to search?' he asked impatiently. 'The radio was out long before we crashed and nobody had our bearings—the plane's gone down without trace! How in hell are they going to find us?' He rubbed one hand over the back of his greying head and looked at her with narrowed eyes, his mouth tight-lipped as he faced the fact that he really was stranded there for two whole months, as their host promised. 'Damn it,' he swore bitterly, 'how *do* we get off this darned island?'

'As far as I can see, Mr. Shushter, we don't,' Carys told him, and wondered why it gave her so much satisfaction to realise it was true.

He regarded her for a minute with his brown eyes hard and suspicious, then they flicked in the direction of his son. 'I guess you don't care too much, huh?' he suggested harshly. 'You figure on having yourself a time with Mike? Having yourself a vacation at my expense?'

It was a temptation that Carys could not resist, although there were possibly better times and places to have chosen. 'I think it's an opportunity during the two months we have to be here,' she said in a voice that she tried hard to steady, 'to work out my notice, Mr. Shushter. The notice I intended giving you when we arrived in San Diego.'

Mike said nothing for a moment, although it was

plain that the news stunned him, but Karl Shushter glared at her with narrowed eyes that glittered coldly in the bright morning sun and made her shiver despite the warmth of the air. 'Nobody quits on me,' he said in a cold harsh voice. 'You don't know when you're well off, Miss Lane, and you just put yourself in a real nasty spot!'

'I don't see how,' Carys said, a little less certain now that the deed was done.

'No?' The hard eyes glittered at her. 'You serve out your notice here, little Miss High-and-Mighty, and you pay your own way back to the U.K. or wherever you plan to go next! Believe me, I don't pay anybody's fare unless they work for me!'

'Of course not,' Carys allowed in her quietest voice. 'I have enough and to spare for my fare home, Mr. Shushter, I have to admit that you've paid me well while I've worked for you.'

'I'm glad you realise it!'

Mike by now had had time to take stock of the situation and it was plain that he did not like it. He looked at Carys with eyes that expressed as much indignation as hurt, but his mouth looked faintly sulky and reproachful. 'You were going to quit without telling me anything about it?' he asked, and Carys shook her head.

'No, Mike, of course I wasn't,' she denied. 'I'd have told you as soon as I'd made it official.'

'But you can't mean to go back to the U.K.,' Mike objected. 'Not when you know I want to marry you, Carys, you can't!'

'What are you talking about, Mike?' Karl Shushter's hard eyes looked at his son suspiciously. 'What's this about marrying my secretary?'

'Your ex-secretary, it seems,' Mike reminded him. 'And you can't claim to be surprised, Pop, you know I've been taking Carys around.'

His father nodded. 'I know you've taken her out, sure,' he allowed. 'She's a pretty girl and you do as you please within reason, but if you get too serious——'

'I have, and it hasn't done me any good!' Mike told him impatiently. 'She's already turned me down!'

It was only the second time that Carys had seen Karl Shushter outfaced and he looked just as stunned now as when Driff Campbell had told him he was marooned on the island for two months. It gave her a certain satisfaction to note the fact as he stared at her without speaking for several seconds.

'You turned him down?' he asked, and the fact that he sounded more puzzled than angry intrigued her. She nodded, and Karl Shushter shook his head slowly. 'You turned down my son?'

'Yes, Mr. Shushter.'

He narrowed his eyes and peered at her unbelievingly. 'You know what you said no to, girl?' he asked, his harsh voice pitched low. 'You realise what this boy's worth?'

'Mike's very nice, Mr. Shushter,' Carys told him steadily, 'but I can't spend the rest of my life with a man I only like.' She looked at Mike again and shook her head, her eyes expressing the regret she felt for having been so frank. 'I'm sorry, Mike,' she said, 'but I don't love you, although I like you a lot.'

Ever ready to bounce back, Mike looked at her darkly for a few moments before he answered. 'With two months in this paradise, honey,' he told her softly, 'I could make you like me a whole lot more!'

Carys was glad to make her escape when Karl Shushter demanded the company of his son. To discuss the situation was the reason he gave, but Carys knew that Mike would far rather have come down to the beach with her, he had made that plain without actually saying so. Carys had not been invited to join in the discussion, so presumably she was supposed to sort out her own problems in that direction.

Her employer, she was well aware, was still not completely convinced that she had been serious in saying no to Mike's request that she marry him. It would take some time for the full meaning to dawn on him, and in the meantime he was treating her with a kind of wary suspicion.

At any other time or in another place the situation would probably have been fraught with tensions for her, but here, on this quiet little island in the Pacific, the affairs of Mr. Karl Shushter seemed such a long way off and quite surprisingly unimportant.

It was warm and somehow gentle, with a soft breeze blowing off the sea, and the urge to paddle in the sea as she had as a child proved irresistible. Her feet were bare anyway and it was little effort to walk straight into the water. The warm Pacific rippled over her toes and foamed around her ankles in creamy frills and she felt peaceful and content.

'Do you *have* to go barefoot?'

Carys turned quickly, wondering why she should feel rather silly and awkward suddenly because Driffort Campbell caught her paddling in the surf. He stood just above the ruffling edge of the tide, his tall figure disturbingly piratical in cream denims and a dark shirt, his feet in leather sandals planted firmly on the white sand.

'I—I lost my shoes,' Carys reminded him.

She came out of the water, uneasily conscious of her appearance, and his bright blue eyes swept slowly over her rounded figure confined in a simple cotton dress that had been made with Luan's childishly thin shape in mind. It was tight enough to emphasise her own contours to an embarrassing degree and she was only too well aware that the scrutiny she underwent was done with an expert eye.

Driff Campbell was a rather disconcerting man in every way, she thought. That strong, tanned face suggested ruthlessness and sent trickles along her spine, and the direct way he was looking at her with those bright blue eyes did strange and uneasy things to her senses. He seemed to belong on this lonely little island, while the rest of them were somehow alien and out of place.

'Doesn't Luan have any shoes you can borrow?' he asked, and Carys shook her head.

'I have rather small feet,' she explained, as if it was cause for apology.

Strong white teeth were revealed in a grin that was quite startling in his brown face, and his eyes crinkled at their corners in that intriguing way she was already beginning to recognise as one of the most attractive things about him. 'You have quite a problem, don't you?' he suggested. 'Her dresses are too tight and her shoes are too big for you.'

Carys acknowledged the fact with an uneasy shrug. It was difficult to answer matter-of-factly when he watched her so steadily. 'It's just unfortunate that Luan is tall and slim and——'

'Thin,' Driff Campbell insisted with a glitter of amusement in his eyes. 'You're slim, Miss Lane, Luan's still thin—she'll improve in a couple of years.'

He spoke with authority, as if he was an expert on such matters, and his confidence was another disconcerting factor. It suggested that he knew enough about women to make that blue-eyed scrutiny not only appreciative but speculative too, and she remembered Mike's hint that she might be able to get more information from their host as to whether they were as completely cut off as he insisted.

'Mr. Campbell.' The steady scrutiny remained undiminished, but a raised brow encouraged her to speak. 'I—I suppose it really is true, that you haven't another boat here?' she ventured, and licked her lips nervously when he frowned.

'Am I supposed to be hiding one?' he asked quietly, and Carys shrugged uneasily.

'Mr. Shushter—we wondered if you had a—a powerboat perhaps.' She looked much more appealing than she realised, and Driff Campbell's blue eyes recognised it with a faint smile.

'No, Miss Lane,' he said, 'I don't have a powerboat. If I did I'd cheerfully put you and your bosses into it and set you afloat to take your chances, believe me.'

'Oh, *I* do!' Carys assured him hastily, then as swiftly shook her head. 'No, I mean that I know you'd help us leave if you could, but I can't convince Mr. Shushter of that.'

Driff Campbell smiled briefly and shrugged broad shoulders under the dark shirt. 'Too bad,' he said casually. 'He'll learn!'

Carys glanced up at the strong, tanned features warily. Something about him, some aura of basic masculinity attracted her strongly, but at the same time alarmed her and made her wary—a combination of sensations she was not entirely happy about. She was suddenly much more conscious of the skimpiness of Luan's dress on her own more rounded figure, and she felt a warm flush in her cheeks as she shook her head.

'I—I hope we don't prove too much of a nuisance,' she said. 'I mean as far as your working's concerned.'

There was a glint of laughter in the eyes that watched her so steadily, and she felt her pulse become more rapid when he extended a hand as if he meant to touch her. Instead he merely waved it in the direction of the ocean behind her. 'With the whole of the Pacific to choose from,' he said wryly, 'your boss has to land his plane on my doorstep! Sure you'll be a nuisance, Miss Lane, but don't let it worry you—I'll survive, I hope your boss does!'

Unwilling to meet the mocking look in his eyes, Carys followed the direction of his hand and looked out at the shimmering surface of the water. It could be idyllic here, but it was unlikely that she would be given the opportunity to enjoy it—not with their host resenting their presence almost as much as Mike and his father resented being there.

She sighed resignedly and was about to turn back when she caught sight of something that looked familiar, floating on the surface about fifteen yards out. One of her sandals, she knew for certain, had floated to the surface, and if one had it was possible that they both had. It would be marvellous to have their solid cork soles under her feet again, and without hesitation she ran into the water.

The surf looked shallow and the sandal was such a little way out from shore that she had no hesitation; even if she had to swim the last few feet it would be worth it. She heard Driff Campbell call out something as she ran, but she was too intent on retrieving her shoe to take any notice.

It was only when the ocean floor seemed to open up suddenly beneath her that she realised the shout had been a warning. She was a fairly good swimmer, but the water was suddenly so deep that she felt alarmingly out of her depth for a few moments and she cried out as she struggled to the surface again.

'You little idiot!' The voice was close by and Carys needed no second guess to know that Driff Campbell had followed her and evidently meant to help her back, whether she needed help or not.

'I'm——' She gasped, much more short of breath than she had realised, and there was nothing she could do about the big, competent hands that held her suddenly, one pressing her back towards him and the other holding her firmly.

'Relax!' he urged. 'You're O.K.!'

Carys struggled free, then trod water while she recovered her breath. Swinging back the long strands of dark hair that straggled across her eyes, she looked at him, half ashamed of her abrupt rejection of him. 'I'm all right,' she insisted breathlessly, and put out an arm to make sure he kept his distance.

The light blue eyes narrowed against the reflection of sun on the water and glittered at her from below a frown that drew his fair brows together ominously. 'You're crazy!' he declared, his voice flattened by the surrounding water. 'Stark, staring crazy!' A couple of strong strokes and he was beside her again, ignoring the extended hand that sought to keep him at bay. 'What in hell are you trying to do?'

Carys turned over and began to swim leisurely back towards the beach. 'I saw one of my sandals floating,' she told him, almost inaudibly. 'I thought I might be able to recover them both.'

It gave her the same jolting shock when they touched bottom with disconcerting suddenness and her hasty glance downwards brought a smile to the glistening brown features of the man beside her. He stood upright, wading against the tide and brushing back the wet hair from his forehead with both hands. Reaching down, he helped her to her feet and together they walked up on to the dry sand, his fingers still curled into her soft flesh.

'This is a volcanic island,' he told her. 'It's like walking off a mountain top, what you just did!'

Standing with his hands on his hips and dripping with sea water he looked a primitive, pagan figure. His clothes clung close to lean flanks and a broad chest and Carys found him dismayingly disturbing as she did her best to avoid looking at him, an involuntary shiver sliding along her spine like a warning.

'I—I didn't expect it to shelve so suddenly,' she said. The clinging softness of Luan's dress revealed the contours of her slim rounded figure with embarrassing frankness and she was uneasily aware that her companion was fully conscious of the fact.

'I yelled after you,' he reminded her. 'Didn't you hear me?'

Carys nodded. Already the sun was drying out their clothes and there was little danger of their becoming chilled, but she was anxious to change into something dry and a little less revealing. 'I—I did,' she admitted.

'But you chose to ignore me!' Carys looked at him, her chin angled defiantly, a gleam of resentment in her grey eyes, and she drew in a sharp breath when he laughed. Then, without giving her time to argue the point, he took her arm again. 'Come on,' he said, 'let's go and get dried out.'

The thought of walking into the house with him, both of them dripping wet, was something Carys preferred not to do, although she could not have said why. She shook her head vaguely, her eyes hidden by concealing lashes. 'I—I think I'll dry off in the sun,' she told him. 'You go.'

He said nothing for a second, nor did he move, then he stretched out a big hand and stroked its moist palm against her cheek. 'You'll ruin that beautiful English complexion if you do,' he warned her quietly, and Carys hastily sought to stifle the strange curl of sensation that shivered along her spine.

Seeking a distraction, something to bring her back to earth, she looked beyond him and saw Luan coming from the house. 'Here's Luan,' she said in an oddly hushed voice, and he turned to look at the girl hurrying towards them with a wide smile on her pretty, doll-like face.

She was carrying something in one hand that she waved triumphantly as she came closer and Driff Campbell frowned curiously at her. It looked like a pair of shoes or sandals and Carys's first instinct was to shake her head, for Luan's size in footwear had already proved far too big for her.

It took only a moment to recognise that the pair Luan now carried would never have fitted her own long, broad feet and Carys found herself smiling without stopping to wonder who they might have belonged to. It was when she took them from Luan that she saw the expression on Driff Campbell's face and blinked in surprise.

It was hard to believe that Luan's appearance with a pair of women's sandals could embarrass him, but that was how it looked, and she hesitated, her hand outstretched for the shoes. Luan, seemingly quite unaware that both of them were soaking wet, looked at her employer with her almond eyes gleaming wickedly.

'John found these in the closet in Mr. Campbell's room, Miss Lane,' she informed Carys. 'They look like they might fit you.'

Carys's hesitation was only momentary, but it was obvious that something about the sudden appearance of the shoes bothered him, just as it was obvious that

Luan's seemingly simple statement implied far more than the actual words. The shoes were a pretty pale blue leather trimmed with gold, and after a moment she took them, curious now about their former owner.

They fitted perfectly, and she smiled at the girl gratefully. 'They're just right, Luan, thank you,' she told her, and glanced again at Driff Campbell. 'You don't know what a relief it is to have something on my feet again.'

'It was lucky John remembered them,' Luan remarked, and again cast a bright-eyed, teasing look at her employer.

He frowned at her discouragingly. 'I'll have a word with John about poking around in my closet,' he told her sternly. 'You tell him that, Luan, and take that look off your face—you look like a cat that's been at the cream!'

Luan, not in the least overawed by the threatening voice, giggled and looked at Carys, as if inviting her to join in the joke. 'Lucky somebody been here before with small feet,' she observed pertly.

'Whoever she is, I'm grateful to her for leaving her shoes behind,' Carys said, glancing curiously at Driff Campbell.

His rugged features now showed signs of impending anger as well as embarrassment and Carys was already beginning to believe that the little island had not always been the isolated refuge he would have them believe. If Luan was right and the dainty blue sandals had been found in their host's bedroom, then it raised all manner of interesting speculations.

She kept her eyes downcast, mostly because she was

oddly averse to seeing him so embarrassed, but Luan giggled again, and Driff Campbell turned to her swiftly, his blue eyes glittering. 'All right, Luan,' he told her quietly but firmly, 'get back to the house. You've had your fun, now get out of here before I forget I'm a gentleman!'

'Yes, Mr. Campbell!' She glanced once more at Carys and her dark almond eyes sparkled mischievously. 'If John finds anything else likely to fit you, Miss Lane,' she said, 'I'll let you know, huh?'

It was too much to resist, and Carys smiled. 'Thank you, Luan.'

'Get out of here!' Luan ran hastily out of reach when he aimed a mock blow at her and ran, giggling, back to the house.

For a second he watched her go, then slowly he turned back to Carys and she was faced with the scrutiny of those piercing blue eyes again. She smiled nervously, conscious once more of the clinging wet clothes she wore. 'You don't mind—you don't object if I have these, do you?' she asked, indicating the shoes she now wore, and he shrugged.

'Why should I?' he demanded shortly. 'They don't belong to me!'

'I thought perhaps——'

'You think what the hell you like, Miss Lane,' he told her quietly but with a hint of harshness. 'I have to put up with you and your friends for the next two months, but I don't have to like it, and I don't have to have you prying into my private life, is that understood?'

Carys caught her breath, resenting his harshness

44

in turning on her. 'I wasn't aware that I'd done any prying, Mr. Campbell,' she told him in a small and not quite steady voice. 'I'm sorry, but I didn't realise that—that a pair of shoes could be such a touchy subject.'

'It isn't!' he denied swiftly. 'I just don't take to strangers making uninformed judgements about me, O.K.?' He ran one hand through the thickness of his blond hair, already drying in the sun, and the blue eyes glittered down at her in a way that stirred some small, secret fear in her, making her shudder. 'Now if you'll excuse me, Miss Lane,' he said with deceptive coolness, 'I'll go and dry off. I have work to do even if it is under difficulties!'

Carys said nothing, but she watched him stride up the white-sanded beach with a certain misgiving in her heart. In the beginning she felt he had resented her own presence just a little less than the other two, now it was apparent that she was as unwelcome as anyone else, and somehow she regretted it more than she cared to admit.

CHAPTER THREE

MIKE had been complaining again about how uncomfortable his bed was, and Carys felt a little guilty when he held forth to her about it, for she had thought nothing more about the sharing scheme she had suggested to him on their first day on the island. For more than a week now he had said nothing about the discomfort he was suffering, or claimed he was suffering, and she had thought no more about it.

Last night, however, he had apparently suffered another sleepless night due to his temporary bed and he made no bones about complaining loud and long, and mostly within his host's hearing. Not that Driff Campbell took much notice of his complaints, although he did flatly refuse to even consider turning John and Luan Kanaka out of their room when Karl Shushter hinted at it.

Carys herself had been sleeping well ever since she arrived, and that fact added now to her suddenly troubled conscience when she thought of Mike and his father still delegated to the comparative discomfort of their makeshift accommodation. For the first time since her arrival she found herself unable to fall asleep straight away, and she wondered if it could possibly be the thought of Mike that was keeping her awake, for she felt strangely restless and not in the least sleepy.

The windows of the little guest room stood wide

open and softly on the night air she could hear the shushing sound of the surf with, somewhere in the background, the lighter, more gentle sound of falling water—the waterfall that Mike had told her was the only means of taking a bath.

She had not so far summoned enough courage to find it for herself and sample its spartan delights, for its reported lack of privacy deterred her as well as the prospect of taking a bath in what she suspected would be very cold water. So far she had managed well enough with the bowls of warm water that Luan supplied her with, but the moment could not be delayed for much longer.

She thought back to the days when she had taken a hot shower for granted every morning, and wondered if she missed some of the privileges of civilisation as much as Mike and his father did. There were so many compensations on the island that sometimes things like readily available baths in hot water seemed rather important compared to the advantages, though she knew well enough that her two fellow castaways would never agree with her. It was a pity, she thought, that they could not enjoy the sheer peace and beauty of Isleta del Tambor Dorado as much as she did.

Startled out of a daydream by additional sounds, she turned her head on the pillow when someone in the big, all-purpose living room next to her own stirred noisily. Shifting furniture creaked and suggested that someone beside herself was restless and unable to sleep, and she wondered if it was Mike tossing on his sun-bed again. Moved by some unquenchable qualm of conscience, she got out of bed and stood

47

by the open window for a moment, looking at the shadowy scene outside.

There was a moon, a big, bright silver moon that etched every tree clearly against the purple midnight sky and gave a look of dark water to the patch of open ground at the back of the house, where the old iron pump stood like a one-armed idol near the back door. There was a kind of magic about this little island that she had found nowhere else, and she almost wished they might never be found, although neither Mike nor his father was the ideal companion in such a situation. Driff Campbell now—— She snatched herself hastily back from that dangerous realm of speculation and looked for something to wrap around herself.

Since Luan appeared to possess no nightwear of any kind, Carys had been unable to borrow anything and she was obliged to sleep in the same natural state that Luan did. But without even a robe to cover herself with she could not move from her room, and another restless creak from the room next door decided her suddenly. She would offer Mike the bed and she would spend the rest of the night on the verandah.

It was much too warm to worry about getting chilled out there and tomorrow she would arrange with him to leave the sun-bed on the verandah for her. It was rather unfair, she decided, for her to have the sole use of the one spare bed and it would ease her conscience considerably if they took turns in using it—herself, Mike and his father.

She took the cotton quilt from the bed and wrapped it around herself sarong-fashion, leaving her shoulders bare, and tucked it in under her right arm, making sure it was secure before she made her way across the moonlit room. It would never do for her to trip and wake the whole household.

Cautiously opening the door into the central passage, she peeped out. Of course there was no one about, but the narrow passage, being windowless, looked discouragingly dark and gloomy after the moonlight in her room, and she hesitated for a moment before going out. She was half way to the big room door before she realised that she was barefoot, but she had not the inclination to go back, so she went on, her bare feet whispering softly on the rush matting.

If she was careful she need not disturb her employer, she could simply tell Mike to go along and take possession of the guest room, then curl herself up on the verandah outside. There was a big wicker-work chair out there that would serve her purpose for tonight.

In the big room the moonlight was even brighter after the gloom of the passage, and she spotted Mike's heaving form as soon as she pushed open the door, the sun-bed creaking in protest under him as he tossed and turned. She must have looked like the ghost of some island beauty, for Mike sat up suddenly and stared at her coming across the room towards him.

The light, flower-patterned quilt wrapped around her like a sarong hiding her slim shape, and her long dark hair covering her bare shoulders, she pattered across the matting on her bare feet, and it was a second or two before he realised who she was, then she heard him release his breath in a great sigh.

'Carys!' he whispered as she came right up to him. 'What are you up to?'

She bent close so as to keep her voice as low as possible and whispered in his ear, 'Take the bedroom —I'll go out on the verandah.'

He stared at her for a second, his brown eyes dark and glistening in the moonlight, then he shook his head. 'No, I can't!'

Carys pressed a hasty finger over his lips when the more solid form of his father stirred uneasily on the chaise-longue, then put a warning finger to her own lips, enjoining silence. 'Go on!' she whispered urgently. 'Please, Mike!'

He glanced over at his father, then at her makeshift sarong, and put a hand to her waist, his fingers curling into the thin quilt and encountering her softness under it. 'Why don't you come——'

'No, Mike!'

She backed away, shaking her head, and Mike looked at her for a moment as if he would debate the point, then he shrugged, and briefly she saw the gleam of his teeth as he swung his legs out of bed, drawing a blanket across his body as he did so. 'O.K.,' he yielded softly, and bent his head as he stood up, to plant a light kiss on her mouth. 'Thanks, sweetheart!'

'Hurry!' she insisted, but he reached for her again with his free hand and she stepped back hastily.

'Carys——'

'Go *on*!' she urged in a whisper, and once more he shrugged and pulled his blanket around him.

Watching him walk away in his makeshift robe, she had the almost irresistible desire to giggle and hastily stifled it with a hand to her mouth as he closed the door behind him. Then glancing warily at her employer she tiptoed across to the outside door and opened it carefully.

It creaked softly and admitted a long shaft of moonlight that was so bright it was like turning on a lamp, and she slipped out quickly and closed it again, listening outside for a moment to see if she had disturbed the lone occupant. A bird somewhere chittered softly among the trees, but there was no sound from the house, and she presumed that Karl Shushter slept more soundly than his son did in their temporary accommodation.

Outside on the verandah it smelled lusciously of bougainvillea and, more surprisingly, the scent of oranges too, mingled with a dozen other scents she could not identify. The surf seemed louder out here too and had a strangely lulling effect that she felt was bound to help her sleep once she made herself comfortable.

The chair was in one corner of the verandah, an old-fashioned wickerwork one furnished with soft down cushions covered in faded flower print, like the ones inside. It looked invitingly cosy and she found it plenty large enough for her to get right into it with her quilt tucked in around her.

There was nothing scary or chilling about sleeping outside, not here on this paradise island and, in contrast to her restlessness inside, she found that her eyelids began to droop after only a few moments curled up snugly in the vast embrace of the old chair.

*　　　*　　　*

It felt very much like a finger, just touching her cheek gently, and Carys turned her head slowly without opening her eyes, her mouth curving into a smile because the sensation of stroking gentleness was pleasant and she did not want to waken yet. Then it touched her mouth, tracing the outline of her parted lips and over on to her cheek again, and she stirred reluctantly, stretching her arms upwards and opening her eyes. Staring hazily at the tall figure standing over her, she frowned while her sleep-dazed brain struggled to identify him.

'Oh!' Recognition dawned at last and she sat up hurriedly, hastily reaching for the quilt which had fallen back and showed most of one slim bare leg. 'Good—good morning!' She drew her legs up under her and covered them with the quilt, feeling strangely defenceless.

Driff Campbell stood for a moment looking down at her, his fair brows drawn into the shadow of a frown, his light blue eyes narrowed, as if he was trying to decide what reason she had for leaving the comfortable bed he had provided for her in favour of a chair on the verandah.

The light denims he wore served to emphasise the length of his legs and there was a suggestion of muscular power about him that was infinitely disquieting at such close quarters and so soon after she had been woken from sleep. A pale blue shirt was opened wide down the front, swinging back from the smooth golden broadness of his chest and a flat narrow waist, and Carys found him a disturbing caller so early in the morning. If only she could have woken earlier she could have got back into the house and wakened Mike before their exchange was discovered.

'What's wrong with your bed?' he asked bluntly, and Carys shook her head.

'The bed's fine,' she told him, shaking back her long hair. 'I—I just didn't think it was fair that I should have the exclusive use of it.'

'So that *is* where young Shushter is!' His eyes gleamed between narrowed lids and he ran a hand through his thick blond hair, brushing it back from his forehead. 'I noticed he was gone when I came through just now and I thought——' He shrugged and Carys was still too drowsy to question his meaning. 'Who organised the swop?' he asked, and Carys blinked at him for a moment, then shook her head. It was too bad of him to ask so many questions before she was properly awake.

'Oh—it was my idea,' she said, and saw a faint twitch of amusement curve his wide mouth briefly.

'Uh-huh!'

He sounded doubtful, and Carys felt she should probably explain what they had in mind, so she sat on the very edge of the big chair with her quilt wrapped round her, feeling rather small and insignificant before his towering figure. 'I know there isn't room for us all,' she said, 'but it seemed more fair and—and reasonable if we take it in turn to sleep in the proper bed. I know Mike hasn't been sleeping very well, so I let him have my room last night.'

'While you slept out here?'

'Of course!' She tried not to read any implication at all into that question.

53

'And he was quite happy to let you sleep out here on the porch while he had your bed?' he asked, and Carys nodded, albeit a little hesitantly, for Mike had raised very little objection to the scheme either when she first suggested it or last night when he had tried to persuade her to share with him.

'I was perfectly all right out here,' she told him. 'I slept well.'

'So I noticed!' She recalled that gently stroking finger on her mouth and prayed the warmth she felt in her cheeks suddenly did not show. He had the disquieting ability to make her feel small and very vulnerable and it was not a situation she enjoyed. He folded one of his arms over the other, his strong hands clasping his upper arms as he raked her again with those disturbing eyes. 'And how long is this—swop system to go on?' he asked.

'I don't know.' She shrugged, thinking that if only he was not standing so close she would get to her feet and perhaps then she would feel less overpowered. 'As long as we have to be here, I suppose.'

'Two months?'

Carys nodded. 'If that's as long as we have to stay.'

He sat back on the top rail of the verandah, his arms still folded and apparently finding nothing at all discomfiting in the fact that she was dressed in nothing more substantial than the quilt from the guest room bed. He produced a pipe and proceeded to fill it with tobacco that he took from the pocket of his denims.

'Do you have any alternative?' he asked as he puffed a cloud of blue smoke into the still morning air. 'We're too far from Hawaii for even young Shushter to swim, even if he is as good as he says he is, and I hear that there's unlikely to be a search party out for you—at least for a while.'

Carys nodded, reluctant to admit that on the whole she wasn't really too unhappy about it. 'When they do search it will be in the wrong area,' she told him, and Driff Campbell's bright blue eyes crinkled as he smiled, a hint of malice in their depths.

'So I hear,' he said quietly. 'I guess you could call it a kind of poetic justice!'

'I suppose you could,' Carys agreed.

The silence that fell between them had a curious kind of expectancy, and Carys sat on the very edge of the old chair, a small pulse throbbing urgently at her temple as she clung to the enfolding quilt as if her life depended on it. 'You—you don't mind if we share the bed in the guest room?' she ventured at last, and one fair brow elevated swiftly on her choice of phrase.

'Not in the least, if you don't,' he told her, then shook his head and laughed softly. 'Forgive me,' he said, 'but I can't help feeling that Mike Shushter must have been pretty optimistic last night when you offered him the guest room—I guess he had you figured wrong, hmm?'

He spoke quietly, almost gently, but those bright, light eyes glittered with meaning through a haze of tobacco smoke, and it was pointless to pretend she did not follow his meaning. He had resented being teased by Luan about the sandals her husband had discovered in his bedroom cupboard, but now it seemed he was trying to suggest that much the same situation existed in Mike's case—and involved Carys.

Determined to quash any ideas of that sort, Carys stuck out her chin, her grey eyes sparkling as she stood up at last, clutching the quilt to her breast and uneasily conscious of her bare shoulders and the precariousness of her only covering. 'I can assure you that you won't find any of *my* shoes in *Mike's* wardrobe, Mr. Campbell,' she told him breathlessly. 'Either here or in Honolulu!'

For a moment she thought he was simply going to overlook the remark altogether, and that, somehow, would have been more embarrassing than anger. But when he laid down the smoking pipe on the verandah rail beside him, she could see that the knuckles of his hands were quite taut and every movement was studied, as if he held his temper only with difficulty, and the gleaming brightness of his eyes sent a shiver through her.

'I'm unlikely to either prove or disprove that,' he told her in a deep cool voice. 'I don't consider it any of my business!'

Carys glanced hastily at the door of the house, wishing desperately that someone, anybody at all, would come and rescue her from what had become an impossible situation. She had never felt so badly out of her depth before and she had walked into the situation simply because she had suspected criticism where probably none had been intended.

He had, after all, suggested that Mike had misjudged her, and when she remembered Mike's suggestion last night, she was bound to recognise that he was right. She had misjudged him as Mike had misjudged her and she glanced up briefly at him, wondering if she could rectify the situation.

'I—I'm sorry,' she ventured, but found little to encourage her in the rugged features.

'For being bitchily tactless?' he suggested harshly, and Carys flushed, curling her hands tightly.

'If—if that's how you see it,' she allowed in a small breathless voice. 'I didn't exactly mean——'

'You enjoyed seeing Luan bug me the other day,' he went on relentlessly, 'and you figured I was getting my own back, didn't you? You figured I was judging you by what you see as my standards—well, believe me, Miss Lane, pretty as you undoubtedly are, I'd like to see you squirm right now, but *you* put the idea into my head!'

Without giving her time to speak he reached out and gripped her shoulders suddenly, pulling her towards him until she was pressed against the warm resistance of his body. His mouth was hard, and determinedly stifled her startled attempt to cry out, while his hands cradled her head firmly when it was forced back against his strong fingers by the fierceness of his kiss.

For a moment her head spun dizzily while she tried in vain to draw a breath, then he let her go suddenly and so unexpectedly that she almost fell backwards, her hands leaving the warm contact with his chest, and instinctively clutching the quilt again. He glanced over her shoulder, then briefly bent his blond head again, his mouth close to her ear.

'See how you enjoy being reminded of *that* at some future date,' he whispered harshly, and stepped back, his light blue eyes crinkling into a smile as she tried to make sense of his meaning.

Before she could find a reply, however, Karl Shushter's flat, cool voice spoke from the doorway, and Carys realised suddenly what he meant. 'What's going on here?' her employer demanded, as if he had caught two of his employees misbehaving in office hours.

Carys spun round, drawing a sharp breath, then as swiftly turned back to Driff Campbell, her eyes wide and reproachful. 'You knew——' She shook her head after a second, realising the futility of berating him, and for an instant she thought she detected a glimmer of remorse.

Then he sat back on the verandah rail again and retrieved the still burning pipe from beside him, as if nothing untoward had happened, nodding politely at Karl Shushter. 'Good morning,' he said quietly. 'Did you sleep well?' Carys, after a brief, helpless look at her employer's curious gaze, turned and hurried into the house in search of some clothes.

'I could cheerfully take a poke at him right now,' Mike said morosely, although he showed little sign of having any enthusiasm for the idea. 'Who does he think he is?'

Carys shrugged. Karl Shushter, of course, had seen fit to mention that short but startling kiss that Driff Campbell had bestowed on her earlier that morning, and Mike had come to ask her about it almost at once, demanding to know what it was all about. It was not so easy to find an answer, Carys found, because she was not quite sure exactly what lay behind the kiss, although obviously he had foreseen it causing her some embarrassment.

'It would be a bit pointless to—take a poke at him, as you call it,' she told Mike. 'There's absolutely no reason for you to get so annoyed about it, Mike. Far better to just ignore the whole thing!'

'And let him get away with kissing my girl when she's not even half dressed?' Mike demanded. 'Not a chance, Carys—I don't like that guy taking liberties just because we're stuck on his darned island and can't get away!'

'All the more reason for keeping the peace,' she insisted, 'and he won't be taking any more liberties, I can assure you!'

She would have felt better if she could have been as sure as she sounded, but this morning Carys had felt herself quite alarmingly aware of Driff Campbell as a very attractive man, and the prospect of being thrown into contact with him for close on two months raised disturbing questions in her mind. He was no woman-hater, that much was certain, and she had no illusions about her own susceptibilities.

'Well, I shall stick with you everywhere you go from now on,' Mike promised grimly. 'He won't get the chance to pull any more stunts like that!'

'You can't come with me this afternoon,' Carys told him with a smile. 'I've finally got up enough nerve to go and use that prehistoric shower system, and I don't want anyone coming on me unexpectedly, so I shall depend on you to keep everyone else away while I'm there.'

'I'll certainly make sure Campbell doesn't follow you,' Mike assured her. 'Though he's probably so used to living like a caveman I guess he doesn't observe the niceties—he'd probably take that open air bathtub in his stride whoever's using it!'

Carys looked at him anxiously, her courage almost failing her again. 'You won't let—anyone go in that direction, will you, Mike?' she asked, and shook her head slowly. 'Maybe I shouldn't use it after all.'

'Sweetheart, you'll be O.K., I promise you,' Mike told her, taking her hands in his and kissing her fingertips. 'It's a pretty crude way of taking a bath, but it's so warm it's actually enjoyable once you get started.'

Intrigued, mostly by the novelty of the idea, Carys allowed herself to be convinced. 'I'll try it,' she said, 'while you stand guard.'

Carys made her way through the trees guided by the sound of falling water, the same sound that had provided a constant background for the other sounds of the island for more than a week now and had so often intrigued her that the wonder was she had not yet sought its source.

During conversation she had learned from Luan that the pump at the back of the house which supplied the kitchen was served by the same powerful freshwater spring that fed the falls, and Carys wondered if ever such a tiny island had been better provided by nature with the facilities for survival.

Once clear of the trees that surrounded the house she found herself in a thick growth of shrubs and undergrowth running riot over the yellowy brown soil that seemed to merge suddenly with the white-sanded beach. There were several orange trees which she suspected must have been planted by some earlier resident of the house, for the present occupier had allowed them to run riot and their fruit was small though none the less fragrant hanging among the new blossom.

There were several different kinds of berries growing too, but she resisted the temptation to sample them in case they were not as good as they looked, and further on she found palms bearing the great green husks of coconut. The flowers too were exotic like those she had seen in the Hawaiian islands—hibiscus, oleander, ginger, and the red-flowered ohia, all flowering in a wild profusion of scent and colour that made her head spin.

The yellow rocks she had glimpsed at from the house towered before her as she made her way through the tangle of vegetation and looked much higher than she had realised, while the sound of falling water was even more audible as it plunged downwards. Although it must have been several hundred miles from Hawaii, the island had a lot of the same characteristics, as if it had been dropped as an afterthought into the deep blue Pacific.

The bare rock was deeply cleft where it jutted above the surrounding vegetation and it gleamed like gold in the sun, while the waterfall emerged from the cleft in a gushing stream and dropped downwards to vanish from her sight in a brilliant rainbow shower. It was several more minutes before she came across the pool, suddenly and almost unexpectedly.

It was formed by a shallow rock basin that made a natural bath, even though it was fairly exposed and all too easily overlooked. For all its drawbacks as a bathroom it was beautiful, and Carys stood for several minutes at the rim of the basin watching the plunging water send up a pluming spray of diamond-bright drops that glittered in the sun.

A rugged slope of steep rocks came down either side of it covered with sparse green bushes and she realised suddenly that it might be possible to climb up to the top of the fall and look out over the ocean —if one had the necessary nerve and energy. It was while she was speculating on this aspect that she caught sight of someone actually on his way down, moving with all the agility of a mountain goat.

It took her only a second to recognise that the blond head belonged to Driff Campbell, and as she recognised him so, it seemed, he noticed her, for he raised a hand and waved it casually as he negotiated the steep rock face. His appearance banished all thought of taking a bath in the pool, but she stood and watched him as he came, admiring the skill and ease of his descent.

Somehow each time she saw Driff Campbell there seemed to be something else about him that she had not noticed before. That lean, agile body, she thought, must be in excellent condition for him to drop down the steep rock with such apparent ease and, not for the first time, she speculated on how old he might be, for such a man was difficult to date.

In the softer light indoors he looked several years less than out here in the harsher brilliance of the sun.

Now, as he came towards her, she guessed he was something between thirty-five and forty, although physically he was the equal of a man ten years younger. There was a muscular vigour in the hard body and a clearness in the light blue eyes that belied an approaching forty years, but there was a maturity in his manner of almost arrogant self-confidence that confirmed it.

His eyes were already narrowed against the bright sunlight as he came down the rock, but they crinkled at their corners when he looked at her, as they always did when he smiled. Dark blue slacks hugged his lean flanks and a white cotton shirt exposed half of the broad, deeply tanned chest beneath it. He ran the fingers of one hand through his hair as he came the last few yards and she noticed the power in the bare brown arms and the long strength of his hands. He was a dangerously attractive man, virile and forceful, and she must do something about her increasing awareness of the fact.

He glanced curiously at the rolled up towel she carried when he joined her, and raised a brow. 'Are you thinking of swimming?' he asked. 'It'll be warmer in the sea.'

Carys shook her head. She had been quite certain that he was in his room when she left the house and she had been trusting to Mike's vigilance to make sure she was undisturbed while she bathed, now it seemed she had been mistaken. When she thought of how easily he might have caught her if he had been only a few minutes later, she could, even now, curl up with embarrassment.

By glancing at the falls behind him she avoided his eyes. 'I—I was going to have a bath—a shower,' she told him. 'Mike says this is the place—you told him we had to use the waterfall, he said.'

Driff looked faintly surprised for a moment, then that expressive brow once more flicked upwards and he shook his head, his eyes glinting with laughter as he looked at her. '*You* don't have to,' he said. 'If you mention it to Luan she'll fix up a tub in your room for you.'

For a second Carys stared at him uncertainly, wondering if the privilege of privacy was hers alone or if Luan was granted the same prerogative. 'But you told Mike——'

'Sure,' he interrupted, 'but I figured we were a little tougher than the girls and not so sensitive about being seen in our natural state.' He indicated the rolled towel she held. 'Were you really going to dunk in the pool?' he asked.

Heaven knew why she flushed so warmly, or why she so hastily dropped her gaze, but she felt that same sense of vulnerability she had before when she was alone with him. Leaving him, she walked off a couple of paces to the edge of the pool and stood looking down into the clear cool water as it lapped against the edge of the rock.

'I was under the impression this was the only means of having a bath,' she told him, her voice unsteady. 'I—I don't expect any privileges, Mr. Campbell.'

'No?' The soft-voiced question had the sound of provocation and Carys turned swiftly her eyes bright with uneasy defiance.

'No!' she insisted. 'I don't want to put Luan to any extra trouble!'

He held her gaze steadily for a moment, and she felt that curling sensation in her stomach again. 'O.K.,' he said, 'don't let me stop you, if you want to take a cold bath—help yourself.'

Carys hesitated, her usual self-possession deserting her yet again, something which seemed to happen with increasing frequency lately. 'It isn't that I don't appreciate the offer of a bath in private,' she told him, 'but if——'

'If you have a bathtub in your room and Mr. Karl Shushter hears about it,' Driff guessed, 'he'll raise merry hell, right?' He laughed, without giving her time to agree or not, a deep warm sound that was infinitely disturbing.

'Not necessarily,' she denied, although the supposition was most likely correct.

'You know he would,' Driff argued confidently, and shook his head, smiling. 'Say, is *every*body scared silly of him?'

Resenting the implication with regard to herself, Carys stuck out her chin. 'Obviously *you're* not!' she retorted. 'But you don't work for him, you don't know what he's like!'

'I can guess,' he told her quietly. 'He'd scare the pants off most people whether they worked for him or not.' The light blue eyes were watching her steadily and she fought against looking at him. 'It's a little like putting Daniel into the lions' den, putting a little thing like you to work for Karl Shushter,' he observed, and Carys shrugged uneasily when she remembered

65

that by the time their stay on the island was over, she would no longer be working for Karl Shushter.

'Actually—as a matter of fact, I shan't be with him for much longer,' she said, and for several seconds the blue eyes studied her thoughtfully. Unable to stand the scrutiny she turned back to the pool, standing with her back half turned to him. He must be pretty well aware of Mike's feelings for her and he would be curious to know what future she had in that direction.

'Young Shushter won't like that, will he?' he said coolly, and Carys turned again swiftly to deny that it was any of his business, but somehow the words did not come, and instead she shook her head slowly.

'Mike—wants to marry me,' she told him, and immediately wondered what had made her confide in a complete stranger.

He was watching her narrowly when she glanced up at him and she wondered what was in his mind. 'It figures,' he said quietly, 'but I'll bet Papa Shushter doesn't go for the idea of his son and heir marrying his secretary—is that why he fired you?'

'He did *not* fire me!' Carys informed him firmly. 'I gave him notice, I've been thinking about it for some time. The fact that Mike asked me to marry him has nothing to do with my leaving. Mr. Shushter knows that I turned Mike down, but it wasn't for that either!'

Driff said nothing for a moment and Carys wondered if he was as stunned as Karl Shushter had been at the idea of a girl like her saying no to all that Mike Shushter had to offer. 'You're quite a girl,' he said

66

quietly, and Carys found herself blushing like a schoolgirl.

'If you don't mind, Mr. Campbell,' she said, sounding a little breathless, 'I'd like to change the subject.'

'Sure!' He smiled at her with crinkly blue eyes. 'Are you really going to take a cold bath?'

Carys looked at him, her eyes wary and wishing there was some way she could remain composed and cool instead of feeling so flutteringly uneasy. 'I—I think I'll accept the offer to have one in my room,' she told him, and glanced up at the towering rock behind her. 'I don't like the idea of perhaps being overlooked—I'm just surprised to realise that that place is accessible.'

'The drum?' he asked, and Carys frowned curiously. 'It's easier from the other side, the incline's more gradual, but it can be done from here, the way I came down.'

'The drum?' She looked up again at the soaring golden yellow rock behind her and Driff laughed softly at her surprise.

'The Golden Drum,' he reminded her. 'See how it's shaped? Smooth and round in front like that—seen from the deck of a ship some distance out, it looks exactly like a big golden drum in the sunlight— hence its name.'

'Isleta del Tambor Dorado!' She repeated the Spanish name inexpertly, and he nodded.

'It's less of a mouthful in English,' he said. 'The Spanish treasure ships christened it when they used to put in here for fresh water, but it's been inhabited only for the last eighty years or so. An old sea captain had it before me, a weird old guy by all accounts, who thought he might find some of the Spanish treasure—at least one galleon's known to have foundered here during a typhoon.'

Carys turned and looked at him steadily for a moment, a hint of smile touching her mouth softly. 'Is that why you bought it?' she asked, and Driff shook his head slowly.

'Not me, honey,' he told her softly. 'But if you want to dig for treasure, go right ahead!'

That 'honey' had a curiously intimate sound and Carys felt the warmth of colour in her cheeks as she shook her head. 'I wouldn't know how to begin,' she told him, and laughed a little uncertainly, 'but it's an intriguing thought!'

He looked at her steadily for a second, then one long hand reached out and his fingers gently stroked her cheek, the same disturbing caress that had woken her that morning. 'I guess you'd be wasting your time anyway,' he told her. 'If there was any treasure to find, the old captain would have found it.' He regarded her for a moment, one brow raised. 'If you've changed your mind about having that cold bath,' he said, 'shall we walk back to the house?'

Hesitating only a second, Carys nodded, and made no objection when his fingers curled over hers as he led her back through the scented tangle of shrubs. It seemed such a natural thing to do somehow.

CHAPTER FOUR

IT was almost four weeks since their unscheduled landing on the island and, in the case of Mike and his father, nerves were beginning to fray. It was only to be expected in the circumstances, for both of them were used to leading a much more active life than of late.

Accustomed to the busy social round of Honolulu and the mainland cities, Mike found the peace and quiet of the island life quite alien to his taste, and his good-looking features were beginning to show signs of boredom. Carys had become good friends with Luan during the past weeks and she sometimes helped her in the kitchen or did chores around the house, but while her help was welcomed by Luan, Mike took a less favourable view of her activities.

He expected her undivided attention now that his father had no call on her services and made no secret of the fact that he disliked being refused, however gently, whenever she put him off with the plea that she was helping Luan. She looked across the table at him now, and thought how much their four-week sojourn on the island had changed him.

There was a sulky droop about his mouth and his brown eyes looked at her reproachfully whenever she caught his eye. So far Karl Shushter had not objected to her domestic activities, but he doubtless would if Mike complained to him about it.

Following their agreement, the three of them, Mike, his father, and Carys, took turns in sleeping in the bed in the guest room, but Carys suspected Karl Shushter was more than a little reluctant to relinquish his occupation now that the time had come. If he did refuse she was unsure just what she could do about it, for technically she was still in his employ, even though circumstances made it impossible for her to carry out her normal duties.

She was usually fairly capable of coping with her employer's harsh character, but she did not in this instance relish the idea of turning him out of a bedroom he had laid claim to, and she wondered if by being ready to share her room she had lost it altogether.

The whole household ate their meals in the big room at the front of the house. Simple meals for the most part, prepared by Luan in the rather primitive kitchen and served on an assortment of plates and dishes, because the house was not equipped to cater for three extra people. It had been obvious from the start that Karl Shushter neither liked nor approved of Luan and her husband sitting down to meals with them, but Carys prayed that even he would never be tactless enough to say as much within their hearing.

It was a remark of Luan's one lunch time that eventually brought matters to a head regarding the shared accommodation. She asked Carys if she would be moving back into the guest room that night, and Carys, glancing at her employer, saw the sudden blank stubbornness of his expression—a look she was all too familiar with. He said nothing, but she had a good idea before she spoke how things would turn out, she thought.

'I—I'm not sure,' Carys said, and hoped that for the moment Luan would not press the matter.

Luan's almond eyes, however, looked at her enquiringly, her doll-like face blandly innocent of causing discord. 'But isn't it your turn?' she asked, and Carys smiled a little wanly, wondering if Karl Shushter would stake his claim openly and now, or if he would simply ignore the fact that his agreed time was up and just carry on as he had been.

He said nothing at all, but sat morosely eating the delicious fresh lobster that Luan had prepared, and it was left to Mike to give her a clue to his father's intention. He glanced uneasily at him as he spoke and there was, Carys thought, a certain artificiality about his smile when he looked at her.

'I think Pop figures on staying put for a while, Carys,' he told her, obviously not enjoying the situation. 'You know how it is, sweetheart.' He laughed uneasily and again glanced at his father. 'Pop's paying you to work for him, and in the circumstances he feels——'

'I figure I don't have to sleep rough while my secretary has it soft,' Karl Shushter said shortly. 'I pay the piper, Miss Lane, *I* call the tune—O.K.?'

Carys was aware that Driff Campbell was watching her narrowly, as if he expected her to argue the matter, but in fact she was already almost resigned to it. Although it made her angry it was no more than she had expected and it startled her to realise, when she looked at him, that Driff was much more angry than she was herself. It was the first time she had seen him so, and it was unexpected enough to make her heart skip a beat.

'I already called the tune when I put Carys in the guest room,' he said quietly, and the use of her christian name came as another surprise, for he had never used it before. 'If she wants to give you turns about,' Driff went on, 'that's O.K. by me, but for Pete's sake be man enough to move out when your time's up!'

Karl Shushter's sharp, handsome features flushed so dark a red that Carys caught her breath in alarm. He was, she knew, subject to high blood pressure and it could eventually lead to coronary trouble if he did not follow doctor's advice and take things more easily. Losing his temper with their provocative host would do no good at all and it would be awful if he were to be taken seriously ill while they were still unable to call on medical aid.

His hard grey eyes glared at Driff down the length of the table and he took several moments to find breath enough to reply. 'Nobody tells me how to treat my paid help!' he said harshly. 'If they don't like it, they can always get out!'

His voice was flat and cold and Carys shivered. She had heard that same voice reduce more than one employee to hasty obedience, and she could not help speculating on how Driff Campbell would react to it. Outwardly he seemed unperturbed, which was what she expected, but a glitter in his eyes gave a clue to his true feelings and there was a slight edge on the coolly calm voice when he spoke.

'I think you have it all wrong,' he said with deceptive quietness. 'What I say goes on this island, Shushter, whether the paid help is yours or not.'

The effect on Karl Shushter was dramatic; he almost shuddered with temper and his hands curled tightly on the scrubbed wood table. Then he flicked a brief, scornful look at Luan and John Kanaka. 'I guess a man who has his servants sit at his table doesn't have much know-how about the way to treat paid help,' he jeered. 'You do it your way, Campbell, I'll do it mine!'

John Kanaka's dark, good-looking face flushed as he rose to his feet and there was a hurt, tearful look on Luan's pretty face. The look in John's black eyes made Carys shudder even though it was not directed at her, but Driff Campbell was, as ever, in charge of the situation and he put a restraining hand on John's arm, persuading him, silently, to sit down again. Refusing to raise his voice, even now.

'This is John and Luan's home,' he said. 'John and I have eaten at the same table ever since he joined me straight from school and I don't intend turning away old friends to make room for uninvited and unwelcome visitors!' His eyes glittered with the same fierceness as John Kanaka's, despite the quietly controlled voice, and Carys found her heart pounding heavily within her, aroused by some deep and as yet unidentifiable emotion.

There was an arrogance about the man, a fierce and unrelenting pride that came to the defence of those closest to him as readily as to his own, and somehow it struck a responsive chord in Carys. It seemed to arouse a sense of belonging, as if she was more closely

73

allied with Luan and John than with Mike and his father.

Karl Shushter looked as if nothing would suit him better than to get up and walk out, but he had nowhere to go to escape the jurisdiction of the man who watched him with such evident scorn and dislike. He sat for some time with a mug of coffee in his hands, hunched and morose, seeing no way out but the boat that would not be there for another four weeks at least.

'When that damned boat comes——' he muttered, and Driff shook his head slowly, his eyes narrowed as he looked at him.

'You still don't get the picture,' he told him with dangerous softness. 'Whether you leave on the *Water Bird* or not depends on me.'

For a moment Karl Shushter simply stared at him, shaking his head, refusing to believe what his instincts told him was the truth. 'You can't mean that you own the ship that's coming to take us off?' he said hoarsely, and Driff nodded.

'That's it exactly,' he told him. 'I keep a sea-going yacht in Honolulu harbour and lay on my own supply line. None of the regular shipping lines come near the island, so you leave here on my say-so, Shushter, and not on the strength of your cheque book this time!'

He imparted the news with such satisfaction and Karl Shushter look so utterly defeated that for one incredible moment Carys felt almost sorry for him. 'So you've got me over a barrel,' he muttered, but Driff was again shaking his head, a hint of smile on his mouth.

'Not really,' he told him. 'I'll be too glad to have you go to try and do anything to stop you, believe me!' He looked again at Carys, a curious gleam in his eyes, an almost wolfish look about the white teeth that showed briefly in the rugged brown features. 'In the meantime,' he said quietly, 'if you can't have the guest room, Carys, I could offer you my own room, although I guess that wouldn't go down too well, would it?'

'No, it damned well wouldn't!' Mike informed him shortly, giving Carys no opportunity to answer for herself. He looked at her uncertainly, a flush on his good-looking face that resented the suggestion. 'We'll leave Carys in the guest room, the way it started out!' He must have thought he detected signs of disagreement from his father, for he waved his hands in a firm gesture of dismissal. 'No way, Pop! We let Carys have the room and we sleep out here!'

It was the first time she had heard him directly defy his father, and Carys found the idea of his doing so now for her sake rather touching, no matter if his support was rather belated. Karl Shushter, for the moment, seemed completely stunned by the whole thing and he said nothing for several seconds but sat with the coffee mug between his hands—silent and grim.

'It seems I'm outnumbered,' he muttered, looking at his son as if he found his defiance hard to believe. 'O.K., we do as you say, though God knows why I've let myself be talked into giving way.' He looked at his host again, narrow-eyed, but more puzzled than vindictive, as if he only now began to realise that he had met his match. 'I guess I know when I'm licked,' he acknowledged, and Carys wondered why she felt so incredibly pleased to hear him say it.

Carys feared it was too much to hope that the matter of the guest room would be allowed to rest, and sure enough Mike brought it into the conversation that evening. He was both unhappy and resentful, she could tell, and somehow she felt that it was partly her fault, although she could not have said exactly why.

He walked beside her along the shore, just above where the surf rolled up in soft waves and ruffled like cream lace frills over the white sand. There could surely have been no more idyllic setting for an evening walk, and yet there was little in Mike's manner to suggest romance even though his left arm encircled her waist.

His frown had scarcely moved since the exchange between his father and Driff Campbell at lunch time, and it was obvious that he was becoming increasingly unhappy with their situation. 'The nerve of that guy!' he said, his hand tight on Carys's slim waist. 'First he talks to Pop like he was just anybody, then he makes that suggestive offer of his room—who does he think he is?'

'There was nothing suggestive about offering me his room,' Carys denied, trying to keep a sense of proportion. 'And as for his manner towards your father, Mike, it's something a lot of people would do if they had Driff Campbell's nerve! It's one of the things that made me want to leave him—that unchangeable belief that his cheque book will buy anybody! It doesn't go down well with a lot of people, you know, Mike.'

'Most people don't talk so big when it comes to the point,' Mike argued. 'Campbell's just making a play, that's all.'

'Making a play?' It was pointless to pretend she did not know what he was hinting at, but she preferred not to recognise it.

'For you!' Mike declared flatly. 'You can't claim you haven't noticed it, Carys, it's too obvious!'

'Not to me,' Carys denied, and for the moment saw it as the truth. So far Driff Campbell had done little to suggest he found her attractive except to kiss her once, and that, she suspected, had been done more with the intention of agitating Karl Shushter than for any more personal reason.

'Oh, for Pete's sake!' Mike said impatiently. 'He kissed you, didn't he? Do you think he did that just for the experience? Be your age, honey, you know Campbell's type as well as I do!'

It was almost inevitable, Carys realised, that sooner or later there would be contention between them, and almost as inevitable that Driff Campbell would be the cause. The wonder was that it had not happened sooner, but for all that she regretted it. She looked up at him, his good-looking features a softer version of his father's harsh handsomeness, and wondered how long it would be before the same harsh principles invaded his, so far, better nature.

'I wish you wouldn't make mountains out of molehills,' she told him quietly. 'Mr. Campbell only kissed me because——'

'*Mr.* Campbell?' Mike taunted. 'Why so formal, honey? He uses your christian name!'

'He's never done it before today,' Carys told him, her cheeks flushed. 'And I suspect it was done with the intention of annoying you!'

'Then he succeeded!' His arm still encircled her waist, but they walked in silence and she sighed inwardly at the idea of quarrelling seriously with him.

The sun was getting low and the sky had that deep, luminous look that she had grown used to in Hawaii, as if it was a great eye waiting to close. It was much too peaceful and too beautiful to quarrel with anyone, and especially with Mike who was surely more unhappy than vindictive. He was a young man, rich and spoiled and sheltered from the unpleasant things in life, and it would be unfair to expect the same strength of character in him as in a man of Driff Campbell's maturity and experience.

Mike brought them to a halt after a while, and turned her to face him. Briefly he looked down at her, and there was a kind of desperation in his brown eyes, then he pulled her against him, his arms tight around her. His mouth had a hardness she had never experienced before when he kissed, and it seemed almost as if he was trying to prove something, though whether to himself or to her Carys was bewilderingly uncertain.

'I don't intend leaving this godforsaken island until you promise to marry me!' he told her. 'I swear it, Carys!'

His kiss left her oddly breathless and she struggled

to free her hands, placing them squarely on his chest and feeling the heavy, urgent beat of his heart under her fingertips. He felt warm and vibrantly alive, and there was no doubt that he was a very attractive man. He was also wealthy and likely to be even wealthier when he inherited from his father, but no matter how she tried she could not convince herself that he was the man she could spend the rest of her life with.

'Please,' she begged softly as she glanced up at him. 'Mike, please believe me when I say I—I can't marry you.' She did not look at him while she said it because each time she had told him so before he had looked so hurt that she felt a twinge of guilt. 'I like you, Mike, but I—I just don't love you.'

'Am I so hard to fall in love with?' he asked, and Carys shook her head.

'Not for the right girl,' she said softly. 'But I'm not the right girl for you, Mike.'

He bent his head again and pressed his lips to her neck, a hard, fervent pressure that sought to convince her, his fingers holding tight to her dark hair. 'I think you are,' he argued in a taut, harsh voice, 'and I'm determined to have you, Carys!'

She looked up at him again, her eyes searching his face, trying not to recognise an echo of his father's ruthlessness in him. 'It would sound much more persuasive if you said you loved me,' she told him quietly, 'but I don't want you to say it when you don't mean it, Mike—and you don't. In a way it's a relief that you don't, because then I don't have to feel so badly about turning you down.'

Unlike his father, Mike was not usually given to

anger, but now he looked both angry and violently resentful of her refusal to give him the answer he wanted. His brown eyes had a deep, angry darkness that made them appear almost black, and they were narrowed as he looked down at her.

'O.K.,' he said flatly, 'have it your way, honey. You go for a romantic stroll on your own—I don't stay where I'm not welcome!'

'Oh, Mike!'

She stood and watched his resentful figure walk away from her, wondering, deep down in her heart, whether she really wanted him to come back to her. If she called him again he would surely think she had had a change of heart and she did not want to start that misunderstanding all over again.

She shrugged after a few moments, then turned and went on her way. What was the point in running after someone she had no option but to see every day of the next four weeks anyway?

It was getting dark with the customary suddenness it always did in this part of the world, and Carys supposed she should think of going back to the house, but the thought of sitting with a sulky and resentful Mike in the one available living room deterred her. Instead she sat on the cool sand with her arms hugging her raised knees, and gazed at the sea.

The moon had not yet made its appearance. When it did the full splendour of her surroundings would become evident yet again. The sea would gleam like dark shot silk, more deep indigo than black, and streaked with silver, and the white sand would shine like crystals.

She picked up a handful of sand and let it run through her fingers, her mind going back to the picnics she had enjoyed on the beach with Mike, the fun they had had. It all seemed so far away now and for a moment she felt almost tearful about it. Being in Honolulu with Mike had been like being part of another world, and she doubted if she would ever know such days again once she left Karl Shushter's employ.

Her own nostalgia made her restless and she shifted uneasily, curling her legs up under her and resting her weight on one hand as she gazed at the placidly rolling ocean. It was almost dark now and a light breeze stirred her dark hair, tickling her neck so that she tossed it back impatiently.

'Carys.'

She turned her head swiftly at the sound of the voice, soft-spoken and curiously gentle. Driff Campbell had a knack of catching her unawares in circumstances like this and she found it infinitely disturbing. She looked at him for a second without speaking, then half smiled, wondering if his being there had anything to do with her own solitary presence or whether he too was simply out for an evening stroll.

'Hello,' she said, and did not realise quite how dejected she sounded until he pulled a face.

'Have you ever been to Copenhagen?' he asked, and Carys frowned up at him curiously.

'No,' she said. 'Why?'

He seemed so overpoweringly tall standing over her the way he was, and she was glad when he brought himself down nearer her level, squatting beside her on his heels, his eyes watching her quizzically. 'You look exactly like the Little Mermaid curled up on her rock,' he told her with a hint of a smile. 'Gazing out over the sea and dreaming of her unattainable lover.'

It was perhaps just a little too close to the truth to be comfortable, and Carys shook her head hastily. 'I was daydreaming,' she admitted, and carefully avoided that cool steady gaze he watched her with.

'But your lover isn't unattainable, surely, is he, Carys?' he asked softly.

She was thankful it was almost dark when she felt the warm colour that flooded into her cheeks and she tossed back her hair again, a gesture that had an oddly defiant air as she gazed out at the shimmering sea. Taking up a handful of sand she let it sift through her fingers slowly as she answered him.

'You seem to be better informed than I am, Mr. Campbell,' she told him, an edge of defensiveness on her voice. 'If you're referring to Mike, he *isn't* my lover!'

'Have you just told him that?' he asked, then immediately held up a hand to stem the answer she had ready. He shrugged, but he was watching her still and she was quite alarmingly aware of his nearness. 'He came back to the house about half an hour ago,' he said, 'and judging by his expression I guess you had a fight—right?'

Unwilling to talk about anything to do with Mike at the moment, Carys shrugged with deceptive carelessness. 'Not really,' she denied. 'We came out for a walk, but——' Again she shrugged, this time in regret because she had not yet had her walk, although it had been her own fault for sitting on the beach instead.

She half expected Driff to probe further and she was prepared to snub him if he did; instead he rose again to his full height and stood for a second looking down at her. Then he reached down with one enormous hand and smiled that slow half smile again. 'Do you still want to walk?' he asked, and Carys looked up quickly, her eyes big and shiningly curious in the dying light.

Then without a word she took the proffered hand and he pulled her to her feet, the movement bringing her into brief contact with him. It was a slight, light touch of their two bodies, but Carys gave a small gasp of sound and drew back even though he still held her hand.

'Perhaps—perhaps we should go back,' she suggested, oddly breathless suddenly, and Driff's darkly tanned face revealed a fleeting glimpse of white teeth when he smiled.

'Perhaps we should,' he agreed coolly, 'but I don't think we will.'

He held on to her hand firmly, as if to thwart any idea she might have for going back to the house alone, and Carys's heart fluttered warningly as she fell into step beside him. They said nothing, but there was a tranquillity about their silence, a suggestion of contentment that was somehow much more agreeable than Mike's intense company, and she accepted it gratefully.

A half moon climbed into the purple sky at last, and shimmered on the dark water like spilled silver, throwing the dark outlines of trees and rocks into silhouette, and showing Carys the strong, rugged profile of her companion in sharp detail. It was almost as if by consent that they turned and looked at one another, and Driff smiled, tingling her pulses into a response that left her feeling breathless and slightly lightheaded.

'You like it here, don't you, Carys?' he asked, and she nodded without hesitation. In such surroundings it was impossible to deny it.

'It's beautiful,' she said, and turned quickly when he laughed.

'Those were almost the first words you said when you arrived,' he reminded her.

'Were they?' The silence having been broken, she felt suddenly less at ease. 'I don't remember.'

'When I carried you up from the beach,' he reminded her. 'You said, just as you did then—it's beautiful.'

She glanced at him briefly, wondering how he could recall her words so well, and remembering how easily he had lifted her into his arms because Mike had not managed it. It had been inevitable, she could see now, that the two of them would never get along together. It seemed barely credible that it was a whole month ago since they had crashed into the sea and been stranded on this paradise island, a month she enjoyed.

'It *is* lovely,' she insisted, 'I've had no reason to change my opinion.'

'You don't mind a little discomfort?' Carys shook her head. 'You don't miss the beaches and the night life in Honolulu?'

Cary laughed and shook her head. 'I wasn't brought up to enjoy night life,' she told him. 'I was born in a little village in Surrey and I lived there until I was nearly nineteen. I'm a country girl—a few discomforts don't trouble me!'

Those crinkly blue eyes looked down at her for a moment, and he smiled. 'And I had you figured for a town gal,' he said. 'Only goes to show how wrong I can be!'

There was a warmth, a sense of intimacy that seemed to bring them closer together suddenly, and Carys felt her whole body respond to it. Her heart was beating hard and fast and she felt slightly light-headed, as if she was on the brink of something. 'I'm quite happy here,' she told him. 'It's so—peaceful.'

Driff looked at her steadily. 'It's a pity your boss doesn't share your taste for peace and quiet,' he said. 'It would make life a great deal easier for everybody in the next four weeks or so.'

His fingers holding hers were warm and strong, and she wished they need not have brought Karl Shushter into the conversation—he did not fit into the surroundings of a tropical island at all. Not the way Driff Campbell did, and talking about him reminded her of how short their time was getting.

'I—I'm sorry if we've been a nuisance to you,' she ventured, and the enfolding fingers squeezed gently, bringing a sudden urgent increase to her heart beat.

'Why do you work for him, Carys?' he asked. 'Is it the money or the travel? Or is it Mike Shushter?'

Carys raised her eyes, on the defensive without being quite sure why. 'Maybe a little of all three,' she admitted. 'Is that so wrong?'

'Not if it makes you happy,' Driff said quietly. 'But it doesn't always, does it, honey?'

Carys had noticed before how disturbingly intimate the word 'honey' sounded when he used it, and yet she took Mike's use of the mild endearment as a matter of course. Perhaps it was because Driff Campbell's deep, quiet voice made so much more of it than a mere casual endearment, and the effect of it shivered through her.

'I—I wouldn't say that I'm unhappy,' she denied cautiously.

He squeezed her fingers again and smiled down at her, a hint of mockery in the arch of his brows. 'You weren't very happy when I found you just now,' he reminded her, and Carys hastily shook her head.

'But that had nothing to do with—well, with anything except a silly argument I had with Mike.'

'He wants to marry you?' She nodded without looking at him and he shook his head. 'Far be it for me to preach like a Dutch uncle, Carys, but you seem to have almost nothing in common—am I wrong?'

'Not—not altogether,' Carys allowed uneasily. She would far rather not have discussed Mike with him, and she had the disturbing suspicion that he was talking to her like the proverbial Dutch uncle, despite his denial. Their clasped hands swung between them and each movement brought him in contact with her, a shivering contact of their bare arms, and she simply could not see him in the role of mature adviser. 'I—

we had a lot of fun when we were in Honolulu, and before that in San Diego—Mike's fun to be with.'

'Huh-huh.' He looked at her with narrowed eyes. 'But is that a recommendation for a husband, honey?'

She frowned impatiently and shook her head. 'Mike isn't going to *be* a husband, or not mine anyway,' she told him, her eyes reproaching him. 'I wish you wouldn't talk to me as if I was——'

'O.K., O.K.!' He laughed softly and squeezed the fingers he held, shaking his head over her annoyance. 'I guess you find Mike Shushter a touchy subject. So,' he added hastily before she could remark on it, 'we'll *change* the subject, eh?'

Carys could not resist a smile, and she looked up at him and pulled a face, pouting her mouth reproachfully. 'I'd much rather talk about your island—I like it here, as you said yourself, just now.'

'You like the island,' Driff said teasingly. 'That doesn't necessarily include the owner, does it?'

It was an infinitely provocative statement and she wondered why he had seen fit to make it. Her eyes had a deep, shining darkness in the moonlight as she looked up at him. 'I like the owner too sometimes,' she said, and noticed that her voice sounded strangely breathless.

He brought them to a halt just above where the surf ruffled softly over the white sand, and Driff turned her to face him. Carys, doing nothing to resist the persuasion of his strong hands, was drawn into his arms, suddenly aware, in a breathtaking moment, of the warm vibrance of his body and the overwhelming urgency of his mouth as it covered hers, enveloping her, sweeping her along on a tide she had neither the strength nor the desire to stem.

The sound of the surf receded in her mind as she closed her eyes and spread her fingers over the strong, vigorous beat of his heart, her own body soft and pliant to the persuasion of his, and she breathed deeply and unevenly in the few seconds after he released her mouth, resting her head on the broad warmth of his chest. For the moment she made no attempt to wonder how she had become involved in such a situation, nor what it could lead to. She was content simply to be where she was and not worry about anything.

Driff eased her away from him gently and for a moment stood looking down at her, his light eyes unfathomable in the moonlight and she would have spoken if he had not bent his head swiftly and kissed her into silence. It was another voice, hoarse with anger, that broke the silence.

'What in hell do you think you're doing, Campbell?' Mike demanded, and it sounded so incredibly melodramatic it was almost laughable.

For a moment no one answered him and he stood looking at them, his dark eyes bright and angry, then Driff smiled, so cool and calm that his self-possession stunned Carys. 'The inevitable effect of a tropical island and a beautiful girl,' he informed Mike quietly. 'Believe it or not I'm human, Mike!'

Mike liked neither his casual air nor the use of his own first name and he made no effort to conceal it. 'Damn you!' His good looking features contorted in fury and he curled his fist so tightly that Carys wondered a little dizzily if he meant to hit out. 'I saw you from way back,' he told Driff, his voice dry and harsh and quite alarmingly like his father's. 'You'd better watch your step, Campbell—this happens to be the girl I'm going to marry!'

'Is it?' Dazedly Carys noted the cool detached air and found it difficult to believe that this was the man who had kissed her so disturbingly only a moment ago.

'Mike, please!' she pleaded, hoping to avert any actual physical violence. 'You have no need—no right to behave like this. I——'

'I came to apologise for walking off and leaving you,' Mike interrupted, slightly less aggressive now and looking more hurt than angry, which was much harder to contend with. 'I guess I was wasting my time,' he said bitterly, and half turned, as if he meant to walk back alone.

'Oh no, Mike!' Carys knew Driff was watching her, and a small curl of embarrassment brought colour to her cheeks when she realised that he was probably finding not only Mike's dramatics but her own serious-ness rather amusing. He was probably no stranger to situations like this and the thought of it being so made her anxious to leave as soon as she could.

Mike looked at her, hesitating. 'Are you staying?' he asked. 'Or will you walk back to the house with me?'

It was not as easy as she might have wished, to just walk off and leave Driff like that, and Carys hesitated, looking from one to the other, but it was Driff's cool air of detachment that finally decided her. He stood with his hands in the pockets of his slacks, looking at her, his light eyes more speculative than appealing.

'I—I'll walk back with you,' she told Mike, 'if Driff doesn't——'

Driff shook his head, a smile dismissing her hint of apology. 'You go ahead, honey,' he told her blandly. 'I shan't get lost!'

CHAPTER FIVE

LAST night when Carys walked back from the beach with Mike neither of them had said very much, but this morning as she strolled beside him, she thought some mention of last night's episode was almost inevitable. Mike would surely find it too much to resist now that he had had time to think about it.

Last night she had managed to postpone the moment by disappearing into the kitchen for the rest of the evening with Luan. To the accompaniment of a great deal of laughter they had managed to create a dress for Carys from some unused curtains that Luan had found. The result had been better than they expected and Carys was wearing the end product this morning, a soft-skirted, sleeveless dress in dark red with a scattering of little white flowers.

She had gone to bed early too, thankful for the privacy the guest room afforded, and then lain awake for some time reviewing her present situation. There was nothing so very wrong, she decided eventually, about being kissed on a moonlit beach by an attractive man, and Driff Campbell had been right not to take it seriously.

She had, nevertheless, carefully avoided looking at him during breakfast, and she suspected that Luan knew why, or at least had an inkling, for there was a bright gleaming look of speculation in her almond eyes that also took into account Mike's slightly sulky mien.

Carys gave her no opportunity to ask questions, but carefully avoided mentioning either Driff or Mike. She had even left Luan to do the breakfast dishes herself and strolled down to the beach with Mike instead. It all looked so different in the morning light, although no less idyllic.

The sea was a deep azure instead of midnight blue, and the sky was gold-hazed instead of silver and purple, but it was still to Carys the most beautiful place she had ever seen and she could quite happily have stayed there for the rest of her life, given the opportunity.

'I just don't get it,' said Mike, his hands thrust into the pockets of his trousers. 'You didn't look like you even *minded* him—manhandling you.'

Carys, seeing some kind of explanation as inevitable now, tossed back her long hair and sighed. 'No one was manhandling me, Mike,' she argued quietly, 'and to be honest I *wasn't* objecting. Driff was right—it was a beautiful night, this is a tropical island, the air was warm and the setting was perfect. Given all those conditions most men would have acted as he did and most girls wouldn't have objected.'

'So now he's Driff,' Mike jeered. 'Things sure moved fast last night, didn't they?'

Determined to treat the matter as lightly as possible, Carys shook her head slowly, refusing to be angered. 'Driff kissed me,' she said, 'am I supposed to react as if it was the end of the world? For heaven's sake, Mike, I'm nearly twenty-four years old, I'm not —shattered by one kiss!' That was perhaps less than the truth, she realised, but she could not tell Mike that. In fact she was not fully prepared to admit it to herself yet, although last night she would have done so without hesitation.

'I suppose I was partly to blame,' Mike admitted grudgingly, 'I shouldn't have left you. But I didn't realise Campbell had gone out as well until Luan asked where he was, then I realised he'd followed you, damn him!'

Although she found the temptation to believe it almost too much to resist, Carys shook her head. 'I don't believe for one minute that he followed me,' she denied.

'Then you're a bigger fool than I took you for!'

'Mike!' He had never before spoken to her so harshly and she turned on him, her grey eyes shadowed by her lashes, but bright and accusing. It hurt too, to realise that he was so ready to vent his anger against Driff Campbell on her.

'Oh, Carys—sweetheart!' He looked so contrite and so unhappy that she could not help but feel for him. Mike was so completely out of his element, and he was finding it increasingly hard to cope.

She looked up at him and shook her head. 'Poor Mike,' she said softly. 'You really don't like it here, do you?'

Mike looked around him, at the white-sanded beach and the gentle surf. He looked at it almost as if he hated it and that was something she found very hard to understand. 'If this is paradise,' he said, 'you can leave me out—I'll take Waikiki!'

Carys laughed ruefully. 'That's a point we differ on,' she told him. 'I love it here.'

Turning to face her, Mike put his hands on her arms, his fingers digging hard into her soft flesh and betraying the stress he was under. For several seconds he said nothing, but looked at her, frowning as if he sought words that simply would not come. 'Oh, damn it!' he swore helplessly. 'Why don't you marry me, Carys?'

'Oh, Mike, please don't——' She shook her head, unhappy at the idea of having to refuse him again.

But Mike was in no mood to be put off, he pulled her into his arms and held her tightly, and there was a glint in his brown eyes that suggested desperation, so that Carys felt herself shivering as he drew her even closer. 'I love you,' he said, and his voice was deep and husky, anxious to be believed. 'I know I've never said that before and maybe I should have. I don't only want you, Carys, I've thought about it a lot since last night. I love you and I mean to marry you—my intentions haven't changed, it's just that I'm more sure of my reasons now!'

'Mike, please,' she begged, 'don't make me say no again!'

'Don't you have *any* feeling for me?' Mike urged. 'Surely after all this time, Carys honey, you *must* have!'

'Yes, of course I have,' Carys agreed, wishing it was easier to be adamant. 'I've told you, I'm very fond of you, Mike, but I don't love you the way you want me to.'

'Is it because of Campbell?'

Being faced with the direct question like that stunned her for a moment, although she should have expected it in a way. It was simply that she had tried to see her reaction to Driff Campbell as merely the superficial attraction of a mature and very virile man. Looking at it from Mike's point of view set her wondering if she could ever become more seriously attracted to their dangerously fascinating host.

'Oh no,' she denied, hastily dismissing the possibility. 'How could it concern him, Mike? I hardly know him!'

'You've had a whole month to get to know him,' Mike insisted grimly, 'and you've another month of living practically in his lap! If only we could get off this damned island!'

'Well, that's something you have in common with him,' Carys told him. 'Driff will be only too thankful, believe me, to see us leave his island—yes, *all* of us,' she added hastily when she saw him about to argue.

'O.K.,' Mike shrugged, but a hint of smile eased the lines of tension around his mouth. Then he bent his head and kissed her. 'I guess I believe you because I want to,' he said, and, putting an arm around her shoulders, hugged her close. He nodded his head in the direction of the white sandy beach that stretched out before them in the bright sun. 'How about taking that walk we didn't have last night?' he suggested, and Carys nodded, willing enough to change the subject.

'I'd like that,' she said.

It had become a necessity during their stay on the island to make walking their main form of exercise. Not since Driff had found her alone on the beach had

Carys had the opportunity to walk in his company again, but Mike sometimes came with her, although he had much less enthusiasm for it than she had. After nearly five weeks there Carys felt thoroughly at home and her ability to adjust and enjoy their isolation gave her an advantage over Mike and his father, who chafed at both the lack of amenities and the restricted venue.

Carys had done quite a bit of exploring, although nothing too adventurous, and mostly she had gone alone when it involved any amount of exertion. Mike professed himself happier stretched out on the beach as if he was still in Honolulu, and she thought perhaps it was a form of self-delusion that he indulged in from time to time.

Driff Campbell, she gathered from Luan, worked whenever the absence of his uninvited guests made it possible, but Carys could imagine that giving his whole mind to writing was not easy when the big room they all used was the same one he normally worked in.

It was something of a surprise when Mike suggested one day that they should walk as far as the cliffs that rose steeply some six or seven hundred yards along the beach, but she fell in with it readily enough, although when the beach began to run out and Mike suggested that they go on, she eyed the rocks with some misgiving.

They stood in a jagged line, like huge teeth, growing taller and taller as they climbed towards the yellow cliffs, and she spared a thought for her only footwear—the little blue sandals John Kanaka had found for her.

So far her exploring had not included rock climbing, although it was evident from what she had seen so far that most of the island was surrounded by high, inaccessible cliffs like these—it was not only a paradise but something of a fortress as well.

The whole terrain was rocky and mostly uninhabitable except for that gentle little cove where the house was built. There were small dells, like the one that surrounded the waterfall, filled with the same dense exotic vegetation, but mostly the going was hard on foot and was left to a variety of bird life and some small green lizards that Carys viewed with mixed feelings.

The size of the island had surprised her rather, and had given rise to speculation on just how wealthy Driff Campbell must be to own it as well as the sea-going yacht he said he had berthed in Honolulu harbour. He had found himself a little paradise and she could easily appreciate his dislike of having it invaded by largely unappreciative strangers.

The sand petered out at last and only rocks lay ahead of them, tall and dangerous-looking, their jagged points thrusting upwards and discouraging further exploration. Mike, of course, was not easily deterred, having made up his mind, and he urged Carys on when she would have called a halt.

Clambering up on to the first rugged outcrop he stood looking down at her, his brown eyes offering a challenge she would willingly have ignored if she could. 'Coming?' he asked, and Carys hesitated.

'I'm not very good at mountaineering,' she demurred. 'I don't think I'll risk it, Mike. These are the only shoes I have and it won't do them any good clambering over rocks.'

His hands outstretched signalled to her encouragingly, and his smile was inviting. 'Come on, sweetheart,' he urged. 'We needn't go very far, and I promise I won't let you get hurt.'

It was strange, Carys thought, how he could make her feel guilty for refusing him anything, and after a few more seconds' hesitation she smiled resignedly and took his hands, allowing herself to be hauled up on to the rock beside him. 'That's my girl!' He bent his head and kissed her, then laughed, as if his own powers of persuasion pleased him.

Their progress was slow, mostly because Carys was being ultra-careful as the rocks got higher, and at last she called a halt, breathing rapidly and looking back with anxious eyes at the height they had gained. 'I think we've gone far enough, Mike,' she told him. 'I don't want to go too high, and the cliffs drop sheer into the sea only a little further on—we don't really know how safe they are.'

'Coward!' Mike jeered. He was standing about two feet higher than she was and laughing at her nervousness, his hands on his hips, outlined against the yellow rock behind him like a dark statue, his shadow short and black in the morning light.

'Come down, Mike, please,' she begged, watching him anxiously.

He looked so precarious, even that distance up and she suddenly recalled Driff's easy descent from the steep sides of the Golden Drum. She had felt no apprehension then, only a kind of excitement at the ease with which he performed the quite hazardous descent, but somehow Mike seemed so much less secure, less able to cope with his environment, and the thought of any kind of an accident made her blood run cold, for there was no way of getting a doctor if he was hurt. She trembled to think what Karl Shushter's reaction would be if anything happened to his son.

Mike, oblivious of any cause for concern, treated her anxiety with the scornful bravado of a schoolboy and climbed up higher, turning to look down on her as she stood balanced on the ragged spikes of rock that marched ever taller towards the sheer cliffs. 'It's as safe as houses, honey,' he called to her. 'Come on!'

'No, Mike!'

'Oh, for Pete's sake!' Mike said impatiently. 'Nothing's going to happen to you—look, I'll show you!'

He took off again, striding from rock to rock, his balance unsteady, while Carys watched him with anxious eyes, biting her lip. Then it happened, what she had been afraid of. He took another long stride and slipped, disappearing from her view, and she let out a sharp, anxious cry, struggling forward over the sharp rocks to find him.

Her progress was more swift than his but also more painful, because in her anxiety to reach him she took less care. He was already struggling out of the crevice he had fallen into, but his face was pale under his tan, beads of perspiration already forming on his forehead as she helped him to gain the comparative safety of a near-flat surface.

'I twisted my foot,' he gasped, and licked his lips anxiously as he extended his left foot and rested it on the rock in front of him. 'I think it's broken, Carys!'

'Oh no!' It was difficult getting to her knees, but somehow she managed it, ignoring the bruising hardness on her own skin, and taking off his sandal she look at his ankle.

It looked puffy and red and was already beginning to look extremely painful. The only bright spot was that when she removed his sandal to make her examination he flinched instinctively, but he moved his toes. 'Well?' he prompted, his lips drawn tightly, and Carys looked up at him.

'It isn't broken,' she told him, trying to sound certain of it rather than merely hopeful. 'You'll have to stay here, Mike, while I go and get some help.'

'Like hell I will!' Mike swore through tight lips. 'And have Campbell thinking I'm too soft to get back under my own steam? You lend me a hand, honey, and I'll get back somehow!'

'Mike, you can't!'

She looked back the way they had come, and the white-sanded beach looked such a long way off that her heart sank. It was a downward incline too, which would increase the chances of another fall if she tried to cope alone with him, and the rocks looked even more fearsome from above. Mike was only an inch or so under six feet tall and he was quite well built; to try and support him all that way and over such terrain would be inviting disaster.

When she turned back she saw that Mike was

already on his feet, his face set into that stubborn expression with which she was all too familiar. He reached out an arm and put it round her neck, testing his balance as they both rose unsteadily, and biting his lip on the pain it caused him. 'I'm going to try,' he insisted. 'Just lend me a hand—I'll manage.'

Carys, unwilling to appear too discouraging, supported him as best she could, but while the rocks had been tricky for her to negotiate on the way up they now proved impossible coming down and trying to support Mike at the same time. She was panting with the exertion and bruised from hard contact with the unyielding rock, her hand and arms aching from pulling their combined weights across the narrow chasms between the outcrops.

There was still some way to go when she eventually called a halt, removing his arm from her neck and helping him to sit down. She looked down at her scratched and bruised hands and shook her head. 'It's no use, Mike,' she told him breathlessly, 'I can't help you alone—I'm going to get help.'

He looked up at her, his brows drawn, hating to admit defeat but reasonable enough to recognise that what she said was true. 'You'll get Campbell out here,' he guessed morosely. 'For heaven's sake, Carys, he thinks we're enough nuisance now, can you imagine what he's going to have to say if he's brought out to rescue me? Get hold of John Kanaka if you can—at least he won't have the neck to make cracks about having to help!'

'I'll try,' Carys promised.

She made sure he was safe for the moment, then

started down over the rocks again, praying that she would not have to see Karl Shushter first, not until Mike was safely back in the house. He would make a major issue of Mike being hurt, whether it was serious or not, and it would be Carys who would take the brunt of the blame for it, that was inevitable.

It was no less easy trying to hurry over such terrain, but at least she was relieved of the burden of helping Mike along as well, and she took a few seconds to recover her breath when she climbed down on to the sandy beach at last. From there to the house was comparatively easy, although it had never before seemed quite so far.

She saw no one as she came across the beach, but when she was within twenty yards of the house Driff appeared, closely followed by Karl Shushter, and before she had gone another couple of yards they came to meet her. 'What happened?' Driff's light eyes noticed that her bare arms and legs were scratched and bruised and that her new dress was dishevelled, but Karl Shushter registered only the fact that his son had not returned with her.

'Where's Mike?' he demanded, his mouth tight and grim, his cold eyes as hard as ice. 'Where's my son, girl? What's happened to him?'

He sounded accusing, she had known he would, but for a moment she felt the almost hysterical desire to scream at him that it was Mike's own fault that he had been hurt, not hers. She felt anger and resentment flare up in her and, almost too late, realised it was a normal enough reaction to the circumstances.

Instead of screaming at him she accepted Driff's

supporting arm gratefully, and wished she did not feel quite so much like crying suddenly. 'He—he's all right, Mr. Shushter,' she said in a small unsteady voice.

'All right?' Karl Shushter demanded harshly. 'How can he be all right if he couldn't get back here?'

'I mean he's not badly injured,' Carys explained. 'He fell—slipped on some rocks and sprained his ankle, but it isn't serious, I'm sure of it. We walked so far, but I—I couldn't manage him any further, so I left him sitting on the rocks while I came back here for someone else to help.'

Driff's arm around her tightened almost imperceptibly and even Karl Shushter looked vaguely surprised by the information. 'You tried to haul him along over those rocks?' Driff asked, and Carys nodded.

'I—supported him as best I could, but he didn't want to be left while I came for help, so I tried——' She shook her head, quite unconscious of the fact that she was depending more and more on Driff for support because her legs felt so tired. 'Poor Mike,' she whispered huskily, 'he did so want to come back under his own steam.'

Karl Shushter swore under his breath. He was already striding off across the beach, then, having gone several yards, he turned and scowled at Driff, who seemed more concerned with Carys at the moment. 'Well, come *on*,' he called harshly. 'Let's get that boy back here!'

Driff ignored him for the moment. He held Carys's left wrist and was frowning over the blood-stained grazes on her arm. 'No wonder you look all in,' he said, 'hauling a grown man over those rocks. Don't you have any more sense?'

'I—I didn't have much choice,' Carys told him, her voice betraying the shivery sensation she felt at his touch. 'Mike wanted me to help him.'

'Huh!'

The support of his arm was strong and comforting and the strong fingers incredibly gentle on her wrist, but Carys felt bound to remind him that it was Mike who was the real patient. 'You'd better go,' she ventured huskily. 'I'm all right.'

Driff glanced over his shoulder at Karl Shushter waiting impatiently, staring along the beach towards the rocks and unconcerned about anything or anyone except his son. 'You're probably in a worse state than Mike is,' he observed, 'but I'd better leave you for Luan to clean up while I go give Shushter a hand to bring in his son and heir—come on!'

He gave her no opportunity to reply but lifted her into his arms, just as he had on the day she arrived on the island, carrying her into the big room as he had then, and over his shoulder she saw Karl Shushter shake his head in disgust and move off, too impatient to wait longer.

Setting her down carefully on the chaise-longue, Driff retained his hold on her for just a moment longer than was necessary and Carys felt her pulses leap wildly in response to the sense of intimacy it suggested. He did not immediately move away either, but stood looking down at her as if there was something on his mind that he could not quite put into words.

'Please——' Carys looked up at him, her eyes anxious, recalling Mike's injunction that she should send John Kanaka instead of Driff to rescue him. 'Couldn't John go and help Mr. Shushter?' she asked, and Driff cocked a curious brow at her, his eyes narrowed.

'Now I know it isn't because you want me to stay with you,' he told her with a half smile that glistened in his eyes. 'So why are you so anxious for John to go instead of me?'

'Well——' Again Carys hesitated. 'It's Mike, he asked me not to let you come for him because he thinks you'll be annoyed about it—he thinks you'll see it as another disturbance, and——'

'He's right,' Driff told her, and laughed when he saw her expression. 'You're a pest, the whole darned pack of you, but I'm stuck with you for another three weeks, so leaving Mike out there on a rock with an injured foot isn't going to do anyone any good, is it?'

'No, I suppose not.'

'Of course not,' Driff said. He bent swiftly and she was suddenly enveloped in the masculine warmth of his body as he brushed his mouth against hers. 'I'll send in Luan to take care of you,' he told her softly, 'then go and catch up with Papa Shushter!' He turned and Carys, too stunned to say a word, watched him stride across the room to the door, wishing she could make up her mind about him.

To Carys's relief, even his father agreed that Mike's ankle was not broken but simply sprained, but it meant he was to be confined to the house for a while at least with Luan as his nurse, a chore she took to with surprising willingness considering the churlish reception her patient gave her.

It surprised Carys to realise that she missed Mike's company less than she expected to. She had spent the last two days with him, since his father and Driff brought him back to the house, but he was a bad patient and his many complaints about his discomfort and his inability to move about as he wanted to made him a poor companion, and she could only marvel at Luan's patience with him.

Perhaps it was unkind of her, but Carys felt disinclined to put up with him for another day. She decided that she would take a solitary walk instead, even though Mike made almost as much fuss about that as he did about his own helplessness.

She had half expected to have Karl Shushter demand that his son be given the guest room in which to nurse his injury, but at least she had been spared that disturbance. She set off shortly after breakfast, catching Driff Campbell's eye as she left the house and wondering why he should find her decision so amusing. There was no doubt that it was amusement that made his eyes glitter the way they did, and it made her a little uneasy to realise that probably Mike's annoyance was the cause.

Her own minor injuries were healing well, and she was quite well enough to go exploring some part of the island she had not yet visited. Dressed in one of Luan's bright print dresses she looked almost Hawaiian herself, an illusion fostered by the fact that she wore her long dark hair loose and her usually light skin was tanned to an attractive golden colour.

With no sense of urgency she made her way through the riot of vegetation until she came to the clearing where the waterfall was, then spent some time gazing up at the glinting yellow rock that formed the illusion of the Golden Drum. Some day she would perhaps venture up there and enjoy the view from the summit, but she would prefer to make the ascent in the company of Driff Campbell, who knew it well enough to treat it with respect.

By skirting the stone basin below the falls, she found herself in another part of the same clearing, but surrounded by even more dense foliage and with a slightly damper, cooler atmosphere. Beyond it the growth of trees and shrubs looked inaccessible, but Carys was in a mood to venture further today and she pushed her way through the close-growing under-wood, only hesitating when one of the numerous little green lizards that the island abounded with ran directly across her path and startled her.

A little ashamed of her own nervousness, she laughed and shook her head, pushing past a scarlet-flowered ohia tree only to find a branch of white, bell-like stephanotis barring her way, its hyacinthine scent heady on the warm air as she brushed it carefully aside. Once more she paused to wonder how anyone could voluntarily leave this tiny island that nature had so generously endowed.

She found herself in yet another small clearing where the trees crowded so close that little of the tropic sun reached the edges, and tall jacarandas spread their fern-like leaves in a canopy over low-growing ferns making the most of the moist, cool shade. Not one inch of the overcrowded space was wasted, and everything that grew was beautiful in its own way, in a way that was still new enough to Carys to be exciting.

Warm after the exertion of walking and beating her own path through the luxuriant undergrowth, she sank down on to the mossy ground thankfully and looked up at the patch of blue sky showing through the feathery jacaranda leaves.

Even the quiet here was different, soft and gentle, shivering with the distant sound of the waterfall and the even more distant sea, nothing disturbing it but the occasional stirring of the bushes, as if some small creature passed among them. It was this incredible sense of peace that lulled Carys into a feeling of lethargy as she leaned back on her hands, and it was the sudden shattering of it that brought her up quickly, staring up into the trees overhead where a brightly coloured parakeet shrieked his resentment at her before taking off.

Carys was so startled that she cried out, staring at the angry little bird as it disappeared among the tree tops, a hand to her mouth and her heart thudding heavily at her ribs. It took several moments for her to realise how inoffensive her antagonist was, and when she did realise she shook her head and smiled ruefully, annoyed by her own reaction.

There was nothing at all to fear on the island, Luan had assured her of that and so had John Kanaka. They had been born and brought up on the Hawaiian island of Ohau, but even they saw this little island as the nearest to paradise they had so far seen. The little lizards that she viewed so warily John Kanaka handled easily, and had even tried to get her to touch one.

They were quite attractive in a way, she supposed, but their cold skins deterred her from actually liking them and she certainly could not handle them as John did. As if her musings had conjured him up, one of the lizards appeared by her right hand, almost lost in the green surroundings, his hooded bright eyes appearing to watch her, completely still except for the throbbing movement of his throat.

Her first instinct had been to withdraw her hand quickly as she always did, but she managed to summon enough nerve to keep still, and for several seconds they watched one another. Her heart was beating hard in her breast, but she kept still, and the little animal did not move an inch.

Carys was beginning to relax when it eventually made its move and once more she drew in a sharp breath, startled by its sudden swift darting movement as it scuttled out of sight among the ferns. Putting a hand to her throat, she heaved a great sigh, then shook her head slowly, despairing of her own lack of courage.

Unwilling to have it put to further tests, she got to her feet, brushing down her dress and smoothing the skirt before she moved on. It was then that she saw something glittering among the ferns where the lizard had sat and watched her, and she bent down, parting the cool damp fronds carefully before she attempted to pick up whatever it was.

One look was enough to set her pulses racing wildly, and for a moment she stared at her find with wide, unbelieving eyes. She bent again, realising hazily that her hand was trembling like a leaf, and picked up the glittering stone, still not truly convinced that it was what it appeared to be.

In fact it was not merely a stone, a jewel with no setting as she had first supposed it to be; the rest of the find was buried under the soft green moss and she had to dig her fingers into it quite deeply to remove it. The lizard's movements had merely revealed enough of it to betray its whereabouts.

It was a ring—a wide gold band set with a huge green stone that even to Carys's inexpert eye looked real, and she held it in her hand for a long while, just staring at it in wonder. The Spanish treasure that the old sea captain had searched for for so many years came to mind. The supposed treasure that Driff had teased her about looking for if she felt like it—it seemed for the moment as if it might not be such a myth after all, and she closed her fingers over the cool green stone and smiled to herself.

Maybe there would be more to find where the ring had been, but for the moment she was too excited with what she had to search for more, and she wanted to share her excitement with someone else. The someone she had in mind as she made her way through the brush again was not Mike or his father, but Driff Campbell.

It was not very easy trying to hurry as she made her

way back through the crowding undergrowth to the house, but Carys went as fast as she could with her precious find held tightly in her hand, anxious to show it to someone who could reassure her, for she could still scarcely believe it had happened.

As she neared the house she opened her fingers again and looked at the ring once more, lying in the palm of her hand, speculating on its age and its origin. It must be very old—it had that look about it. The mellow, heavy look of antique gold that glowed richly in the sun and clasped the green gem in an old-fashioned claw setting. Her own eyes convinced her it was not only beautiful but valuable, and the possibility of there being similar treasures nearby gave her a strange curling sensation in her stomach.

She closed her hand again tightly and ran the last short distance to the house, her eyes already looking for signs of Driff, her eyes shining. It was not so much the possible value of the ring that excited her so much, but the thought of where it might have come from and the history attached to it. It was almost a miracle that after so long it should have been uncovered, almost by chance, by the activities of a small lizard.

'Driff! Driff!'

She called out as she ran up the step on to the verandah, and she was already half way through the doorway before she realised that Mike was sitting out there, half hidden by the profusion of bougainvillea that covered most of the rails and supports. He sat in the big cane chair she had slept in once, his foot resting on a low stool, and he looked at her frowningly, as if he was uncertain whether to be more annoyed about her calling for Driff or curious about the reason for her excitement.

Her eyes were shining and her cheeks flushed from hurrying, and she turned swiftly when he spoke. 'What's all the excitement?' he asked, and Carys hesitated only a moment before extending her hand.

'Look,' she said. 'Look what I found!' There was little chance for him to see what she held, for she turned almost at once when Driff came out of the house, striding hurriedly in answer to the urgency of her call. 'Driff, look!'

John Kanaka was just behind him and he too looked relieved when he saw her apparently unharmed but excited. He reacted in the same way that his employer did too, when he looked at the ring in the palm of her hand, its green stone gleaming richly.

Mike looked genuinely dumbfounded, and reached out to take it from her, turning it, frowning over it, but it was Driff and John's reactions that puzzled her. They glanced only briefly at the ring, then looked at each other, and something in their expressions made her frown curiously. It seemed incredible to think they recognised the ring, but seeing their reactions she felt almost sure they did.

She took it from Mike and offered it to Driff, her eyes watching his face uncertainly. 'It's very old, Driff,' she said, and wondered how it was that it sounded so much like a plea for confirmation.

Driff took the ring from her, holding it for a moment in his long fingers and turning it slowly so that the green stone caught the light, while Carys looked from one to the other. For a moment no one spoke, and even Mike seemed to recognise that there was something significant in their silence. 'Where did it come from, Carys?' he asked, and Carys still looked at Driff while she answered him. There was something about his manner, and John Kanaka's, that made her uneasy, but she could not yet decide why it was.

'It was while I was out walking,' she said. 'I went through by the waterfall and then on past there into a little clearing. I was hot and I sat down for a while and one of those little lizards came and sat right there near me—I'm jumpy when they come near me and I watched him. It was when he moved away that I spotted the ring where he'd been sitting—he must have uncovered it when he scuttled off.' She glanced at John Kanaka again, but he avoided her eyes and she wondered why. 'It *is* very old, isn't it, Driff?' she asked, and he nodded.

'Yes, it's very old,' he agreed, 'but it isn't what you think it is, Carys.'

She looked at him, shaking her head as the first suspicions loomed in her mind, then she reached out and touched the bright glowing stone with a fingertip. 'I—I thought it might be part of the——'

'No, honey!' His tone of voice, his gentleness when he disillusioned her, brought a frown to Mike's face, although he said nothing for the moment. 'I don't believe in the Spanish treasure story,' Driff told her, 'but I do know about this ring—I'm sorry to disappoint you.'

'You—you recognise it?' Her heart sank, although if she was honest the Spanish treasure story had always been too fanciful to be true. It was just that she disliked the alternative so much that it surprised her.

Driff looked down at the ring in his hand and nodded, but the smile he gave her was both gentle and apologetic. 'I'd let you keep your treasure if it really had been left by the Spaniards, Carys,' he said quietly, 'but it isn't treasure trove, and it isn't mine to give.'

She knew, Carys thought with sickening certainty. When she saw John Kanaka turn and go back into the house, she thought she knew who the ring belonged to and she glanced down at her sandalled feet and, almost involuntarily, frowned. The bitterness that welled up inside her suddenly was not entirely due to disappointment, although she so far refused to recognise the fact. She looked at the ring Driff held and her cheeks flushed as she lifted her chin, a bright glow of resentment in her grey eyes.

'I wouldn't want anything that doesn't belong to me,' she said in a small, cool voice. 'I understand perfectly, of course—the same privileged visitor who left these sandals I'm wearing also left some of her jewellery!' She forgot about Mike sitting there, frowning at her curiously and trying to understand her anger. Instead she looked at Driff with a chaos of jumbled emotions churning away inside her and a suspiciously bright haze in her eyes. 'Well, now you can return it to her, can't you?' she said, and turned quickly.

She walked back down to the beach, her head held high and a strange, inexplicable anger curling her hands into fists as she made her exit, not even bothering to turn when Mike called out to her. Maybe her anger was unreasonable in the circumstances, but it was very real for all that and she sought no excuse for it.

CHAPTER SIX

IT was not difficult to guess that Mike had found her hasty and angry departure the previous day not only annoying but puzzling, and sooner or later he was bound to ask questions. It was with the idea of avoiding those questions that she had stayed carefully out of his exclusive company for the rest of the day. She was not yet ready to admit the reasons for her anger even to herself, and certainly not to anyone else.

Five days of being confined to the house, or at best the verandah, had chafed Mike's restless spirit more than anything else had done so far during his enforced stay on the island. He declared his injured ankle less painful but still too painful to bear his weight, and his mood was one of resentful self-pity.

Even though she would like to have evaded the inevitable questions for longer, Carys could not find it in her heart to leave him to his own devices for another day, so she had agreed to sit with him on the verandah for a while. He occupied the old wickerwork armchair, with his bandaged foot resting on a stool, while Carys perched herself on the verandah beside him, hoping she had the patience to deal with the inquisition.

Her eyes were more often on the silken-smooth surface of the ocean than on her companion, and Mike noticed the fact with a frown. Reaching out for her hand, he pressed it between his own two and looked up at her, his brown eyes appealing as well as curious. 'You don't really want to stay with me, do you?' he asked, and Carys turned quickly to deny it.

One look at his forlorn expression brought a smile to her face and she felt genuinely sorry for him in his enforced idleness. 'What makes you say that?' she asked, then without waiting for an answer, shook her head slowly. 'I have rather neglected you, haven't I?' she asked. 'Poor Mike, I'm sorry!'

He squeezed her fingers, watching her face as he spoke. 'You've been avoiding me,' he accused, 'and I think I know why.' He waited a moment for her reply, then, when it became obvious that she was not going to answer, he shrugged lightly, his fingers twining in hers. 'What's all the mystery about that ring you found, honey?' he asked quiely. 'Come on, tell me why you got so mad about it, huh?'

'I didn't get mad!' The denial was defensive and she realised that to Mike it must appear very much as if she had something to hide, a guess that was confirmed when he cocked his head to one side and narrowed his eyes as he looked at her.

'You bristled like a porcupine when Campbell obviously recognised that ring,' he argued confidently. 'Then you made some snide remark about him giving it back to—I don't know, some mysterious somebody that you evidently knew about and I don't. You stalked off looking like you were about to blow your top—all I'm asking is to be put in the picture, hon.'

'I can't put you in any picture,' Carys denied, 'because I don't know what the picture is!'

'But you know more than you're telling me!'

'Maybe,' she allowed cautiously.

She wished she knew more about the owner of the sandals she was wearing. It was surely not reasonable to dislike someone she had never even met and knew nothing about, and yet she was finding it all too easy to resent Driff's past visitor, and the realisation troubled her.

'Oh, come on, sweetheart!' Mike insisted. 'Who is she?'

The look in his eyes did not match the lightness of his tone, but at the moment Carys did not notice that, and she shrugged uneasily. Absently lifting the perfumed head of a bougainvillea blossom, she inhaled its fragrance, hiding her face for a moment in its cool beauty. 'I don't know anything about her,' she said. 'I only know that she stayed here—I don't even know when.'

'Here?' Mike's brows rose and he pulled a face. 'You mean Campbell *does* have visitors here, after all?'

'It looks like it,' Carys admitted unwillingly. She extended her left foot and regarded the small blue leather sandal it wore with a hint of dislike. 'I know she has small feet and can afford expensive antique rings—nothing more.' Mike was regarding her curiously, his head to one side, and for the first time Carys realised he had never questioned her acquisition of the shoes she wore. 'Luan brought these sandals down to the beach one day when I was talking to Driff,' she told him. 'She—well, she teased him about John finding them in his bedroom cupboard.'

'In *Camp*bell's bedroom?' His lips pursed into a silent whistle and he nodded his head. 'So much for the isolationist author in search of peace and quiet, eh?'

Carys shrugged uneasily. She already regretted saying as much as she had, but it was too late to retract now. 'On the contrary,' she said, 'I believe he *did* buy this island so that he could work here in peace.'

Mike laughed shortly, unconvinced. 'Like hell!' he declared harshly. 'I knew he was too good to be true! The reason he doesn't want us here is because we cramp his style in quite another direction!'

'Oh, for heaven's sake, Mike!' She snatched away her hand and stood up, trembling like a leaf, though she had no good reason for it that she could see. 'It's nothing to do with us what Driff does on his own property!'

'It is when he includes my girl in his plans!' Mike retorted. 'The nerve of the guy—acting like he hates company when all the time he——'

'I don't believe he makes a habit of inviting people here,' Carys insisted, and avoided his eyes, looking instead at the blossom she held between her fingers.

'You think this female was something special, then?' Mike asked, and Carys admitted the possibility only grudgingly.

Pulling the bougainvillea blossom from its vine, she twirled it between her fingers. 'I suppose so,' she agreed reluctantly.

'Hmm!'

Mike was speculating on possibilities, she could

tell that, but she wanted only to drop the subject as soon as possible. 'Can't we talk about something else for a change?' she said, making her reluctance quite obvious, and Mike regarded her with raised brows.

'Sure, if you feel that strongly about it,' he agreed. 'Personally I get quite a kick out of uncovering our host's secret vices, and I'd give a lot to know who this mystery woman is.'

'Well, I couldn't care less!' Carys told him shortly. She was dismayed to realise just how much she did dislike talking about the woman whose shoes she had literally stepped into and she looked across again at the glittering Pacific, shaking her head impatiently. 'I think I'll take a stroll along the beach,' she said. 'I feel like getting away from the house for a bit.'

'You're deserting me?' Mike asked plaintively, and she hesitated. Then, looking at his rather sulky mouth, she shook her head, refusing to be made to feel guilty in this instance.

'No, Mike, I'm not deserting you,' she told him, 'I just feel like my own company, that's all.'

'It amounts to the same thing!' His complaint followed her as she walked along the verandah and down the one step on to the white sand without turning her head again. She knew Mike was watching her resentfully, waiting for her to turn and come back to him, and if she did not he would look upon her going as deserting him, and would resent it with all his heart. 'I don't suppose you'll have to wait long before you have company!' he called after her, his voice sharp and accusing. 'You never do, do you?'

Carys refused to even turn and give him the satisfaction of knowing that his jibe had gone home. The more she got to know Mike, the more it surprised her to realise how little she had really known him until now. Being thrown into daily contact with him in conditions that he found adverse revealed a lot more about his character than she had seen before. He had not yet fully grown up, the past week or so had revealed that, and it became quite apparent to her as she walked away from him now that she could never seriously consider marrying him.

His parting words about never being alone for long gave her food for thought, for all that, for it was quite true, although she faced the fact uneasily. She had avoided being alone with Driff, as she had with Mike, since yesterday morning, and she wondered if she could cope with the emotions that Driff could arouse in her. There was little she could do about it if he did join her, she decided eventually, and shrugged resignedly as she walked on down towards the sea.

She sat for some time, just above where the tide rolled in; curled up in her favourite position with her legs tucked under her and her weight resting on one hand. She was uncertain whether she hoped Mike's prophecy would prove true or not, but she knew by instinct who had joined her when a long shadow fell across her suddenly, obscuring the sun.

Her heart was thudding like a hammer in her breast, and she was tempted to look around and see if Mike was watching from the verandah, although he could surely never have really believed that Driff would follow her.

'Carys? What's wrong?' Driff was squatting on his heels beside her, but she did not turn, only glanced up briefly, and as she did so she caught a bright glitter of amusement in his eyes and flushed warmly.

'I simply wanted to sit and watch the sea for a while,' she told him, and turned her head swiftly when he laughed.

His light blue eyes crinkled at their corners as they always did when he smiled or laughed, and his teeth gave the strong, rugged face a wolfish look against his brown tanned skin. His arm brushed hers lightly when he moved and she flinched almost as if she had been burned, the rapid beat of her heart becoming even more urgent.

'You didn't like me keeping your Spanish treasure, did you?' he suggested, and she shook her head to deny it, without actually saying anything. He sat down on the sand close by her, much too close for comfort, his knees bent and supporting his arms, and his eyes were narrowed against the glitter of the sun on the surface of the sea. 'Believe me,' he said quietly, 'if it *had* been the old captain's treasure, you could have had it.'

'Oh, but of course I couldn't!' Carys angled her chin, tossing back her long hair in a gesture that denied any desire to take anything from him. 'And you certainly couldn't give away a valuable ring that must be worth a fortune—I mean, it isn't the same as a pair of sandals, is it? Your—your guest would certainly miss something as valuable as that!'

'It was missed!' One long hand reached out and lightly touched her cheek in a gesture that was almost a caress, and yet she knew that he must be resenting her reply—the meaning behind her words. 'You're so sure I've had a woman staying here with me, aren't you, Carys?' he asked.

Stifling the shiver his caressing finger induced, Carys turned and looked at him for a moment in silence. She was not prepared to admit an interest in his affairs, but the dry half-smile that touched his wide mouth suggested he knew it well enough. 'You surely can't deny it,' she said in a dismayingly husky voice. '*Some*body left these sandals behind and it certainly can't have been a man—nor was that a man's ring. Not,' she added hastily when she saw him about to speak, 'that it concerns me in the least, but I see no point in being secretive about it, that's all. If you want to keep a whole succession of women here, why shouldn't you?'

'Why shouldn't I?' Driff echoed softly, and she noted uneasily that he had made no effort to deny the suggestion.

'I—I suppose you find it embarrassing to admit it, having told us that you never have company here because of upsetting your peace and quiet,' she went on a little breathlessly. 'I suppose that's why you were angry when Luan mentioned the shoes—because it made it awkward for you. Being found out, I mean!'

'Found out!' Driff's great hands curled tightly, and there were other warning signs too that made Carys shake her head in dismay at her own recklessness.

'As I said,' she insisted, 'it's no business of mine *who* you invite to stay here!'

'You're right—it isn't!'

An angry silence hovered between them for a moment, and it was Carys who eventually offered the olive branch, although it came as something of a surprise to her to realise just how anxious she was to appease him. 'I'm sorry,' she ventured, watching him from the corners of her eyes, 'but I couldn't understand why you were so obviously annoyed with Luan for letting the cat out of the bag, so to speak.'

Driff ran a hand through his blond hair. He did not look at her but continued to watch the ocean, his blue eyes narrowed and inscrutable. 'I dislike having situations like that sprung on me,' he said in a deep, cool voice that did little to suggest he was appeased. 'Luan might have found it very amusing to embarrass me by producing those sandals for you out of the blue with an innuendo that even a child couldn't miss, but I didn't share the joke—especially when it was evident you were more than ready to take the bait she dangled so temptingly.'

'I'm sorry.'

He turned and looked at her steadily for a second and his blue eyes regarded her with an intensity that sent a shiver of sensation through her whole being. She was more conscious of him than she had ever been before. More aware of the strong aura of masculinity that emanated from him and touched her like a lick of flame, so that her fingers trembled unsteadily as she sifted a handful of sand through them.

It shouldn't matter that he had had a woman staying with him on the island, but somehow it mattered much more than she was prepared to admit, even to herself, and she stirred uneasily under his scrutiny.

'No one comes here at my invitation except John and Luan,' he told her, 'I want that clearly understood; I work here and work only. What I do elsewhere, the way I—entertain, when I'm not working, might give you the idea that I use this place as a tropical harem, but in fact nothing is further from the truth. It's simply that sometimes, and your own arrival is a case in point, I don't have the choice; things just— happen.'

Carys scooped up another handful of sand and let it run through her fingers, trying to steady the urgent beat of her heart and wishing she was not so anxious to be convinced. 'Driff, you don't *have* to explain,' she said in a small husky voice. 'It doesn't matter, it doesn't concern me, it's your——'

A large hand silenced her and she merely shook her head but complied with its demand. She was to be given no choice, she realised—he would explain the presence of the mysterious visitor whether she wanted it or not. 'I'm going to straighten you out,' Driff told her quietly, 'and you're going to listen, O.K.?' She nodded, for there seemed little else she could do but hear him out.

'I don't know if you know it,' he went on, 'but I have a house in Hawaii as well, on the island of Oahu. But you know Oahu, of course, don't you, having spent some time in Honolulu with the Shushters?' She nodded and he went on without giving her time to say anything. 'You know what island society is like,' he said. 'There's never any shortage of parties and dinners and I come in for my share of invitations.'

'Yes, of course, you would,' Carys said, and he

cocked a brow at her, as if he suspected she was being sarcastic.

'I met—well, her name doesn't matter, at a dinner party,' Driff went on, 'and after that, while I was there we went around quite a bit together.' His light eyes looked at her steadily, but she found the gaze too disturbing to endure for long and stirred uneasily. 'I'm not making excuses,' he told her frankly. 'I like women and——' he smiled, 'for some reason only they know, they seem to like me. Not being a saint I make the most of it!'

'Driff, please!' She looked at him anxiously. It gave her a curiously vulnerable feeling, having him explain. As if he was trying to let her know that even with women of his own choosing he never became too serious about them. She shook her head while her hand drew patterns in the white sand with quick nervous strokes, and as quickly erased them again. 'I'd—I'd rather you didn't explain,' she told him. 'I know what you're trying to say, and——'

'You don't have the remotest idea what I'm trying to say,' Driff interrupted quietly. He reached out to cover her restless hand with his own big one, his strong fingers pressing hers into the sand. 'I don't like the idea of anyone seeing me as two-faced, and that *is* the conclusion you've come to, isn't it, Carys? You've decided I'm somebody who doesn't practise what I preach, isn't that about it?'

His eyes challenged her to deny it and Carys, unable to do so as firmly as she wished she could, simply lifted her shoulders in a helpless shrug of admittance. 'It's none of my business,' she said huskily, and Driff laughed. It was a short and rather harsh laugh and she frowned over it.

'I know that,' he told her frankly, 'but I'm going to tell you about the owner of that ring just the same. Maybe then you won't go stalking off in high dudgeon because you think I've been caught out!'

'Oh, Driff, I didn't!'

She looked at him reproachfully, and once again he laughed, only this time there was more humour in the sound of it, and his blue eyes had a faint glimmer of amusement as he looked at her. 'You should have seen yourself, honey,' he told her, and squeezed the hand he covered, his strong fingers curling over hers tightly. 'Now—will you listen?'

Carys tried to do something about the pace of her heart's beat, and the fluttering sensation of excitement that those strong fingers caused. 'Yes, of course,' she said huskily. 'It's the least I can do, if you want me to.'

'As I said,' Driff went on, as if the interruption had not occurred, 'we went around together quite a lot, although there was nothing serious about it, and when I came back here to work I never gave her another thought. Then, a couple of months later, when the *Water Bird* arrived with the supplies, Elizabeth was on board. She'd bribed my captain to bring her, told him I was expecting her, and he believed her, even though he knows my ruling on no visitors!'

Carys looked at him through her lashes, trying to imagine his reaction to the unexpected arrival. 'Perhaps—maybe she's—fond of you,' she suggested, and realised how gauche the words sounded when he turned and looked at her with one brow raised and a hint of amusement mocked her from the depth of his blue eyes.

'I hardly think so,' he denied coolly. 'But she *was* determined and not used to being told she couldn't have something when she'd set her mind on it. She quite expected me to let her stay once she was here.'

'But you didn't?' She had no real need to ask, Carys thought; in his own way Driff Campbell was every bit as ruthless as Karl Shushter, and the realisation brought a swift shiver of warning for her own susceptibilities.

Driff shrugged his broad shoulders, his eyes narrowed as they once more looked across the bright dazzling surface of the sea. 'I didn't,' he agreed dispassionately. 'She stayed for a couple of nights, just as long as the *Water Bird* was here, then I sent her back to Honolulu.'

'Shipped out as soon as possible—an unwanted nuisance like me,' Carys said impulsively, then hastily bit her lip when she realised how easily he could misinterpret her words.

Strong fingers pressed hers tightly for a second, then he shook his head. 'Not quite like you, honey,' he told her quietly. 'You're a slightly different proposition—and much too easy to hurt.'

Carys said nothing for the moment, but her heart was racing like a wild thing and she wondered if he was aware of it, as he held her hand so tightly. 'I don't merit special treatment, Driff,' she told him huskily. 'I know how much your island means to you and I shan't blame you at all for sending us packing as soon as your boat comes. You must have hated every minute we've been here, hindering you—you've lost so much time.'

Driff's eyes crinkled into a smile and his wide mouth crooked at one corner as he looked down at her steadily. 'Oh, it's had its compensations,' he said, and leaned across to kiss her mouth lightly. For a moment she was enveloped in the vigorous masculine warmth of his body when she came into contact with him, one big hand cradling her head with long fingers, and the sensation it caused shivered through her like a shock. 'In fact,' he observed, his eyes teasing her, 'it's been quite an experience!'

Mike, Carys assumed, would be still sitting on the verandah where she had left him, and she wondered if he had witnessed that brief but disturbing kiss. If he was still there they must have been clearly visible to him and briefly she felt a qualm of conscience for declaring her preference for her own company.

The top of his head was just visible above the verandah rail, but it was apparent he was no longer alone when Luan's unmistakable giggle reached them, and Carys saw the swift drawing of Driff's light brows when he heard it, and detected a slight lengthening of his stride as they approached the house.

There was no sign of either John Kanaka or Karl Shushter, so presumably Mike and Luan were alone. The thick vines of bougainvillea made it difficult to see exactly what was going on on the verandah, but when they were within a few feet of the step Carys saw and recognised that Mike's sudden reaching for

Luan's slim waist was quite deliberately provocative. He pulled the girl down on to his lap and her giggles stopped so abruptly that the cause was obvious.

Driff left Carys's side and hurried on alone, taking the verandah step and several feet of verandah in two long strides. Carys, fearing the outcome, ran after him and got there in time to see Driff drag Luan forcibly from Mike's lap and hold her by one arm while he looked down at Mike narrow-eyed. His mouth had a tight angry look and his light blue eyes glittered like chips of ice as he fought to control an obviously formidable temper.

Then he turned to Luan, his fingers digging deep into her arm, and pushed her towards the doorway of the house. 'Get inside,' he ordered her coldly, 'and thank your stars that John isn't with me!'

'Mr. Campbell——' Her doll-like face with its almond eyes looked at him appealingly. 'You won't— you won't tell John?' she said, and Driff shook his head impatiently.

'I think too much of John to want to hurt him,' he told her, 'or I'd tell him and let you take your chance!'

Luan said no more, she turned and hurried inside without even glancing at Mike, while Driff gave him his full attention. 'I don't have to tell you that John only needs an excuse to give you what's coming to you,' Driff told him in a cold hard voice that matched the glitter in his eyes. 'You and your father have given him plenty of cause to dislike you and what you just did was adding insult to injury, though I guess it was aimed more at Carys than at John!'

Mike had the grace to look slightly ashamed, although he showed a hint of defiance in his thrust out chin too, and his brown eyes resented the dressing down. 'You don't have room to go shouting about taking liberties,' he told Driff angrily. 'How do you think I feel, being stuck here while you follow my girl and——'

'That's enough, Shushter!' Driff warned coldly. 'I know you consider you have some kind of claim to Carys, but she has other ideas, or so I gather.'

He glanced at Carys and she felt the colour flood into her cheeks as she shook her head, but before she could say anything, Mike was taking up arms again. 'She's going to marry me!' he declared. 'I told you that before, Campbell, and it still goes!'

Driff did not even look at him; the light blue eyes still watched her steadily and she tried to put into words her own feelings in the matter. 'It's—it's not true,' she said in a voice that shook anxiously. 'I've told you, Mike, I can't marry you!'

Mike's brown eyes looked both hurt and angry, and he shook his head as if he was trying to dismiss an unpleasant truth he preferred not to hear. 'You'd have married me quick enough if we hadn't landed on this godforsaken island!' he insisted. 'You would, Carys, you know you would!'

'Whether or not Carys would have married you has nothing to do with you playing games with Luan,' Driff informed him coldly. 'Luan's a married woman, no matter how young she is, and John's a good friend of mine. You keep your hands off her in future, Shushter, if you know what's good for you!'

'Does the "keep off the grass" sign apply equally to you?' Mike asked harshly. 'Or do you have automatic rights to every female who lands here?'

'Driff, no!' Carys was not sure whether he would actually have used the big fist that clenched hard in front of him, or if it was merely an instinctive gesture, but she put her own small hands round his arm and felt the steely muscles tense under the warm smoothness of his skin.

He stood for a moment looking down at Mike imprisoned in the big armchair, his eyes like glittering ice, then he put a hand over the anxious ones that held his arm and pressed her fingers reassuringly. Her heart was thudding away at her ribs until she thought she would choke with its stifling beat, and his eyes were on her, glittering and angry so that she shivered involuntarily.

'Don't worry,' he told her quietly, 'I won't hurt him!'

The contempt he put into the words was hurt enough, and Mike's good-looking face flushed at what they implied. Then Driff gently eased her fingers from his arm and held them for a moment in his. It seemed to Carys that he would have said something, but perhaps Mike being there deterred him and he merely shook his head, then strode past her into the house.

CHAPTER SEVEN

It was much earlier than usual when Carys woke the following morning and she lay there looking at the sunlight on the bedroom wall. The little room with its light cane furniture was now so familiar to her that she felt completely at home there. Its one window stood open to the morning air and the sounds of the waterfall and the nearby surf combined in a background that was now as comfortably intimate as that of her own home.

She lay for some time watching as the sun grew stronger, but eventually succumbed to an irresistible restlessness that would not let her rest. It was too early even for Luan to be up and preparing breakfast, but if she was quiet she need not disturb anyone.

Unwilling to go to the trouble of heating water for a bath, she fetched cold water from the pump and washed in that. No one had stirred and when she eventually left her room there was still no sign of anyone, although she thought she heard voices from John and Luan's room. Venturing into the big living room where Mike and his father were, she found them both still asleep and managed to leave the house without waking them.

A solitary walk before breakfast would perhaps still her restlessness besides giving her a chance to think without distractions, and there was a great deal to think about lately. Mike's behaviour with Luan yesterday was one thing, although he had undoubtedly acted as he did with the express purpose of both paying Carys back for that kiss he had witnessed and also making Driff lose his temper.

It was a disturbing incident because it raised new and discomfiting probabilities in the next few weeks. John and Luan had been married only a very short time and there was some ten or eleven years' difference in their ages, so that John was probably more than normally sensitive about his very young wife. If Mike persisted in his behaviour John would not only be hurt but angry too, and with cause—Driff had been right to put a stop to it right from the start.

There was a curious brassiness about the sun this morning, Carys noticed as she made her way through the luxuriant mass of shrubs and trees that surrounded the waterfall clearing. She had not noticed it such a colour before, but she gave it only a brief thought as she walked through to the waterfall, scolded by the angry chattering of the island's noisy, colourful little parakeets. There were other things to think about.

She stood for several minutes beside the hollow stone basin below the falls and looked up at the mellow smoothness of the Golden Drum, drawn to it as she had never been before. In the morning sun it looked as if it really was made of gold, and she could easily imagine the awe it must have inspired in those early Spanish seamen when they first caught sight of it from their ships.

Even from where she stood the name it had been given seemed very apt, for the smooth yellow-gold boulder gleamed like a huge drum from which the water gushed out into the sunlight and fell like a shattered rainbow into the basin below. Its grandeur was every bit as moving as the more delicate beauties of the flowers and trees that surrounded it, and Carys felt a curious affection for it suddenly, an almost personal pride.

For some time, ever since she had first seen the drum, she had thought about climbing up to it and looking out over the ocean, but until now caution had deterred her. This morning, in her present restlessness, caution was banished and she walked around the perimeter of the stone basin to the far side where the incline seemed to be slightly less precipitous. Although for all that she eyed it for several moments before finally making up her mind.

Bushes clustered at the foot of the incline and she made her way through them, standing for a moment to gaze up at the rugged sweep of rocks and scrub that came down either side of the waterfall. Driff had descended with apparent ease and she saw no reason why she should find it impossible to climb up there. There was an easier way, of course, from the other side, as Driff had told her, but she was in no mood to postpone the venture, having made up her mind to it.

Soon after she started climbing, above the sound of the falling water, Carys heard a faint rumbling sound and listened to it for several seconds curiously. She could think of nothing to account for it, but eventually dismissed it as probably being caused by the water falling on to the hollow rock basin below.

Climbing was more difficult than she expected and

she was hardly dressed ideally for it, but the sense of achievement it gave her to be doing it at all made it worthwhile. It was when she got part way up and paused to rest that she began to realise just how hard a task she had set herself.

Supported by the rock behind her, she looked down and saw just how little distance she had come at the expense of so much exertion. Below her the rock basin looked like a man-made pool and delightfully pretty set amid its trees and flowers, but it was not nearly as distant as she expected. Above her lay at least twice the distance again and for the first time she felt a slight sensation of panic at the thought of going down again.

The ascent became more difficult as she went on and she was getting very short of breath, also she noticed a new coolness in the wind suddenly that was quite alien to the island's usual balmy breezes. Possibly it was due to the fact that the higher she went the cooler it got, but it was more forceful too and lifted her hair from her neck and pressed her cotton dress close to her body.

Scrambling on to a fairly flat section of rock, she paused again for breath and turned and looked across at the ocean, stretched out into infinity. It rolled like a bale of rumpled silk to the horizon, but she frowned after a moment at the quite discernible difference in its character since the last time she looked at it.

The waves were no longer lazy and gentle but white-topped by creamy spindrift that sped over the surface, whipped before a strong wind. The bright clear sky too looked much different and there were clouds rolling rapidly towards the island, already obscuring the strangely brassy sun she had noticed earlier. Heavy storm clouds bearing a strong wind before them and the force of tropical rain that lashed the surface of the sea into a frenzy even while she watched. The rumbling sound she had heard earlier she now recognised as thunder, and she crouched against the rock, appalled by her own helplessness.

The storm was coming nearer with a speed that was frightening and the colder wind was already snatching at her hair and her dress and trying to dash her from her precarious place on the rockface. Too suddenly faced with the unexpected, she did nothing for a moment, but watched it coming, until, almost too late, she realised how vulnerable she was in her present position.

There was a big boulder close by and it, to Carys's mind, offered the best shelter, but her anxiety to beat the wind and rain was so urgent that she slipped and stumbled on the rocks as she made her way across to it. She dropped into a hollow behind the boulder at the very moment the rain hit the island, striking hard with an angry hiss as it poured over the warm rocks, the wind beating it down so that it formed a blinding spray that hid everything from sight.

Huddled behind the boulder, she was sheltered to some extent by the scrub that overhung it, but it did not take her long to realise that the hollow she had first seen as quite shallow was in fact a natural basin in which she stood breast high. She had stumbled into it without understanding the implication of its size and she was all too soon made aware of her mistake.

She was wearing the red cotton dress that she and Luan had made and very little else beside, and for the first time in several months she felt shiveringly cold. The heavy tropical rain penetrated even the overhanging scrub and there was nothing she could do but endure the discomfort. Her dress clung to her like a second skin and her hair was slicked wetly to her head, clinging to her face and neck as she stood and shivered.

A depressing fact too was that no one knew where she was. It would probably be assumed that she was oversleeping, although Luan would see she was missing as soon as she took in the water for her bath, but no one was likely to realise that she was where she was—up here on the rockface, sitting out the storm.

She felt isolated and quite alarmingly helpless up there alone, trapped in a stone hollow that was rapidly filling with water and already incredibly uncomfortable. If only she had waited and asked Driff to come with her she would not have been caught like this—but being wise after the event was no use, she had followed an impulse and she must do as best she could now.

Below her the trees bent their heads before the lashing wind and rain and the yellow rocks around her hissed and rattled as if the whole rockface would shatter and fall in the fury. In a way it had a strange element of excitement about it and, even wet and helpless as she was, somehow the fury of it aroused a response in her that bred defiance rather than despair.

Then suddenly it was gone. Almost before she realised it and even more abruptly than it had struck, the storm blew across the little island and left it shimmering like a jewel in the bright sun, every leaf hung with rainbow drops of moisture that rapidly dried in the renewed warmth. There was a fresh earthy smell too, as if the small island had been washed clean and now lay drying in the sun.

Carys could scarcely believe that the whole thing had happened so fast, that the storm had come and gone so quickly, but water reaching as far as her knees was evidence of how fierce the storm had been. The problem remaining was how to get out of the water-logged basin and back down the slope to the house, and Carys had to give it some serious thought.

She hopefully grasped the edge of the hollow with both hands, but although she could reach the edge, climbing out was quite another matter, and her heart was thudding anxiously when, for the third time, her fingers slipped on the wet rock surface and she splashed back into the water.

'I've *got* to!' Carys stood off for a second breathing heavily and gazing at the slippery rock resentfully. The edge was too high for her to get enough purchase to haul herself out, and she was finally forced to face the fact that she really was trapped there until some one found her.

Nothing around her offered any hope of helping herself and she could have wept in sheer frustration. There were no foot or handholds in the rock and the scrub that overhung her head snapped off when she tried to use that, letting her fall back so suddenly that she was completely submerged and came up shaking her head and sputtering angrily.

Carys took a moment to recover her breath and tried to picture the general consternation when it was discovered she was not in the house, though how long it would be she could not guess. Mike at least would be curious, and so, she thought, would Driff. Luan would certainly wonder where she could have got to at that hour of the day, so they would be looking for her, she knew, but how would they guess she was stranded on the rocks, a victim of her own impulsiveness?

She thanked heaven for the blessed warmth of the sun after the cold winds that the storm had brought, and at least the top half of her body would dry in the warmth. Her main concern was to devise some way of letting those below know where she was, and she came to the eventual conclusion that the best solution was to utilise her red dress for the purpose.

It was unlikely that anyone searching below would notice her hands waving, but her dress being red would be less easily overlooked. Unhesitatingly she slipped it off and tried to wring out most of the water. If she held it at arms' length and waved it, someone was bound to see it sooner or later.

It seemed like hours to Carys, standing there waving her red dress and trying to attract attention, so far without success. She had heard no sound other than the chatter of the parakeets in the trees below, and noise of the water tumbling over the falls with renewed vigour since the storm rains.

Her arms ached and she felt like giving up in desperation. Surely sooner or later someone was bound to think of looking for her up there, but in the meantime she was obliged to suffer the discomfort of her rock prison, and she faced the fact resignedly.

She would give it one more try, she decided, and then rest for a while. It was at that moment that she caught the faint but distinct sound of human voices. Standing on tiptoe in the water, she raised her arms above her head and waved the red dress back and forth urgently, calling out, adding her voice to the mute appeal of her improvised signal.

'Driff! Driff!'

It would have to be Driff she heard coming. It certainly couldn't be Mike, and Karl Shushter was unlikely to face such a climb simply to look for his erstwhile secretary. It was Driff, she knew, and probably bringing John with him, since she had heard two voices.

It seemed an interminable time before she heard another sound but that of her own anxious breathing, and she almost resigned herself to the fact that she had been neither seen nor heard. Then a sudden light sound, like a shoe scraping, gave her renewed hope, and she called again.

'Driff!'

'Over there!'

She heard Driff's voice pinpoint her signal and heaved a great sigh of relief. She stood for a couple of seconds with her eyes closed and her forehead resting on her arms, then as the sound of footsteps came closer it came to her that she should put on her dress.

It would simply add to her already acute embarrassment if she was rescued wearing nothing but the flimsiest of underwear. Hastily she pulled the dress over her head, but she was still struggling to get her arms through the sleeveless armholes when Driff suddenly appeared.

He stepped into view on the edge of the stone basin, tall and lean against the blue sky, darkly ominous in navy slacks and shirt, his blond head gleaming like gold in the sunlight. He looked down at her for a moment, as if he could not believe what he saw, and she almost cried out to him not to judge her yet until she was on her own feet again and able to face him.

He said nothing to her, but turned to John when he appeared beside him. 'Give me a hand!' he ordered sharply.

John looked, if possible, even more surprised, but he bent down beside him and four strong hands reached down for her. Carys grasped them tightly and thankfully and they hauled her, dripping wet, from the pool of water. She felt weak with relief and her legs seemed quite incapable of holding her, so that she tottered and would have fallen when she stood at last on the rim of the basin.

In a moment Driff's arm was around her, hard and reassuring, drawing her against the strong warmth of his body, and she leaned against him while his arms held her close, an unexpected surge of emotion bringing tears to her eyes. His face rested on her wet hair and the strong hands that held her soothed and comforted, still without a word being spoken.

Carys raised her head at last, although she was reluctant to leave the haven he offered. 'I—I'm sorry,' she whispered, and looked from one to the other of her rescuers.

Neither said anything for a moment, but both men regarded her with a strange mixture of curiosity and disbelief. It was John Kanaka who eventually broke the silence, his handsome brown features breaking into a smile. 'You're lucky we found you so quick,' he told her. 'We wouldn't have done, 'cept Mr. Campbell spotted that red dress of yours from down there.' He grinned at her quizzically. 'What made you come up here, Miss Lane?'

'Because she's got no more sense than a two-year-old baby!' Driff informed him before Carys could answer for herself, and she felt her heart shrink in the face of his anger. 'What in hell possessed you to come clambering about up here alone and at this hour of the day?' he demanded. 'Are you bent on breaking your neck, or do you just like getting me out on rescue operations?'

Carys shook her head. She felt miserable and uncomfortable and she had thought her ordeal was over when he found her; now, it seemed, he meant to extract the last ounce of vengeance from her for causing him yet more disturbance. She felt close to tears again, but she refused to let him see it or he would probably decide she was crying simply to annoy him too.

'I'm sorry you were bothered,' she said in a small trembly voice, and saw John glance at him curiously, as if he found his anger puzzling.

'Didn't you realise what a damn fool thing you were doing?' Driff demanded, and she shook her head.

'I—I came out for a walk,' she told him. 'It never occurred to me that I could get into this sort of trouble simply by climbing the rocks to the drum— I've seen you do it more than once!'

'Maybe,' Driff agreed, 'but I'm used to it and you're not! If you want to go rock climbing at dawn again, you ask somebody to bring you, don't just go sneaking off before anyone's up, and causing a flap they must've heard in Honolulu!'

Carys still felt shaky, her legs unsteady and threatening to let her down, and she would have given a great deal to have that strong supporting arm about her again, to rest her head on the broad comfort of his chest. In his present mood, however, it seemed unlikely he would allow either and once more she felt like weeping.

His eyes held hers for a second with an intensity that brought a swift urgency to her heartbeat, then he shook his head. 'Let's get you back to the house,' he said, 'before you catch cold!'

Going back down they took the longer, easier way, but even so Carys found it quite hair-raising in places despite the steadying hands that half carried her. They came to the house at last by the back door and Luan let them into the kitchen, her almond eyes wide and anxious when she saw her.

'What did you do, honey?' she asked, taking Carys's arm and glancing at her husband. 'How come you're so wet? Did you get that storm we had?'

John relinquished his interest to his wife, but Driff still had a firm grip on her arm, and he looked down at Carys with a frown between his brows. 'Get her a hot bath and put her back to bed, Luan,' he said. 'We can't have a pneumonia case on our hands, and that rain water's damned cold when you're standing in it up to your knees.'

Carys looked up to protest, but the look in his light blue eyes challenged her to argue and she merely shook her head, following Luan. 'You get to bed, honey,' Luan advised with a gentle concern that sat oddly on her youthful shoulders. 'I'll get your bath water ready.'

Without making sure that Driff was out of earshot, Carys shook her head. 'I'll be glad of the bath, Luan,' she said, 'but I'll dress again afterwards—I'm perfectly all right.'

'Carys!' He came back from the big room doorway, his brows drawn, a warning glint in his eyes. 'Can't you do as you're told?' he asked. 'I can't afford to have another patient making more work for Luan— you get sick and you'll be even more trouble than you are on your feet!'

Carys looked at him, her hands clenched tightly and a bright defiant look in her grey eyes. 'I'm all *right*,' she insisted. 'All I need is a warm bath and I'll be fine—I've no intention of taking to my bed as if I was an invalid, Driff, it isn't necessary and I won't do it!'

'You——' He looked for a moment as if he meant to enforce his decree with physical force, and Carys could sense Luan watching with more than passing interest. He sighed deeply after a few seconds, however, and shook his head slowly, his tanned features shadowed and dark in the dim passageway between the rooms, only his eyes light and glittering and narrowed warningly. 'O.K.,' he said at last, 'but don't you ever do anything like this again, Carys, or by heaven I'll make you wish you hadn't—now go and have that bath!'

It was only a couple of days later that Carys woke up to the unpleasant fact that she had not escaped from her ordeal as completely unscathed as she thought. She woke one morning sneezing violently and feeling so heavy-eyed that there could be no doubt about it—incredible as it seemed in such a warm paradise, she had caught a cold.

Luan noticed nothing when she quickly scurried in and out again, bringing her her bath water, but when she emerged from her bedroom Driff was quick to notice. His room was directly opposite to hers across the narrow passageway and they came from their respective rooms at the same moment. He took one look at her dull, red-rimmed eyes and unflatteringly red nose and frowned.

'Carys?' He put a hand on her arm and looked down at her curiously. 'What's wrong, honey? Why are you crying?'

His obvious concern almost tempted her to keep him in ignorance of the real reason for her watery eyes and red nose, but it was not a deception she could hope to sustain for very long, and Driff hated being fooled. 'I'm not crying,' she denied, with a rather woeful smile. 'I've got a cold, that's all.'

'A cold?' He looked at her so accusingly that she might have confessed to having some horrible disease.

Then he pushed her bedroom door open with one hand and with the other urged her back inside. 'You get right back into bed,' he told her, 'and you stay there!'

Carys stared at him. 'But you can't send me to bed like a—a naughty child,' she objected. His concern gave her a curious sense of satisfaction, but she disliked being ordered to stay in bed.

'If you'd taken notice of me when you came back soaking wet the other day,' he told her firmly, 'you wouldn't be like this. For heaven's sake see sense this time, Carys—go to bed!'

'But it's only a cold,' she insisted, although her resistance was already weakening in the face of his firmness.

'And I'm putting you in isolation until it's gone, my girl,' Driff told her adamantly. The hand on her arm was insistent, but she stared at him, only half believing he could be serious about it.

'Oh no, you can't!' she protested. 'You can't isolate me as if I had—yellow fever or something, just because I have an ordinary common or garden cold. It doesn't make sense!'

'On the contrary,' Driff argued quietly, 'if you stay out of circulation we might not have anyone else going down with it. You stay in your room, Carys, and you won't be breathing your cold germs all over everybody else—that's sense!'

'You're a—a bully!' she accused, her face flushed and her voice growing huskier every minute.

Driff took the accusation in his stride, merely shrugging his shoulders and smiling. 'Maybe,' he allowed.

'But we've no doctor on call if it turns out to be something worse, so you just get back into bed, honey, and I'll send Luan in with some breakfast for you.' His eyes swept over her swiftly and speculatively, then he nodded as if he had made up his mind about something. 'I'll send you in one of my shirts to use as a nightgown,' he told her. 'You'd better have something to put on if you're laid up, we can't have you sneaking about wrapped in that old quilt—a shirt'll be loose and comfortable.'

Carys flushed, remembering the time he had found her on the verandah asleep in the wickerwork chair and wrapped in the quilt from her bed. It seemed such a long time ago now, but she could still remember his kissing her, the gentle finger that had stroked her cheek until she woke up stroked gently across her mouth, almost like the promise of a kiss. There were so many pleasant things she could remember in connection with Driff.

He touched her cheek lightly. 'O.K.?' he asked, and she nodded.

Her spirit rebelled against being ordered what to do, but in truth she felt ill enough not to be completely averse to the idea of going back to bed, and eventually she shrugged her shoulders, and gave in. Sighing in self-pity, she waited until the door closed behind him, then undressed and got into bed again to wait for Luan to bring her breakfast.

It worried Carys to some extent, being out of touch, because she could not help thinking about what Mike must be feeling. Deprived of her company, it was possible he might turn to Luan for consolation again, and that concerned her deeply. The idea would not even have entered her head at one time, she had thought she knew Mike too well to suspect anything like that, but since she had seen him with Luan on the verandah, she realised just what he was capable of if he felt himself neglected.

Luan was a good nurse and she took on the extra chores involved in looking after Carys quite willingly. She was cheerful and pretty and almost childlike in her affection for people so that Carys's fears had verdant ground to grow in. It was almost a relief, therefore, when during her second day of confinement the bedroom door opened slowly and Mike's head appeared round the edge.

He looked at her for a moment with a persuasive grin on his good-looking face, as if he half expected her to send him away, but when she did no more than smile at him a little doubtfully, he hobbled across the room and sat on the edge of the bed. He took her hand in his and looked down at her curiously.

'I've missed you,' he told her. It would not occur to Mike to enquire how she was, she realised, he was concerned only with his own situation. 'What's the idea of Campbell giving orders that you're to be isolated?' he demanded. 'You're not that sick, are you, honey?'

'I've got a very bad cold and possibly a chill in my stomach,' Carys explained. 'I'm not really ill, Mike, but Driff doesn't want everybody else catching it.'

'Was this isolationist thing your idea,' he asked, 'or

was it his? Surely you don't have to stay in solitary with a cold in the head, do you?'

Carys glanced at the bedroom door, thinking she heard footsteps in the passageway outside and half wishing someone would come and interrupt, for she felt so ill and not a bit like arguing with Mike. 'It's just sense, Mike,' she said. 'Colds can spread like wild-fire and we don't want an epidemic. You shouldn't really be here, Mike.'

'Who says so?' Mike demanded aggressively. 'Is Campbell a doctor? He has no right to keep you in your room, Carys, and you should tell him so!'

'Mike, please,' she begged. 'If all of you get colds as well——'

'Ah, who cares!' Mike interrupted impatiently. 'I'm getting sick of sitting about doing nothing and talk-ing to nobody, honey! Thank heaven we've only got another two weeks on this damned island, then back to civilisation—even if it does have to be on Camp-bell's yacht.' He squeezed her fingers and smiled down at her, and Carys recognised the signs all too easily. 'Don't you feel like getting up and coming out in the sun, sweetheart?' he asked persuasively.

Carys put a hand to her hot forehead and closed her eyes briefly. Mike would never understand that a chill was making her feel worse than just a common cold would have done. 'I—I don't feel too good at all, Mike,' she told him, and his brows drew close in a frown, his mouth showing that hint of sulkiness that Carys was beginning to recognise.

'In other words you'd sooner I went and left you to mope on your own, huh?' Carys said nothing and he sat holding her hand for several seconds, his fingers twined restlessly in hers. 'I'm disappointed, honey,' he told her. 'I felt sure Campbell must be keeping you here when you didn't want to stay. Instead it looks like you don't *want* to get out!'

'Mike!' She turned her head, wishing it did not throb so persistently. 'Please don't——'

'Oh, come on, Carys, you've only got a cold!' He put his hands behind her suddenly and lifted her into his arms, holding her against his chest while he smiled confidently down at her. 'You can get up now, hmm?'

He took her by surprise when he kissed her suddenly, and her struggles were instinctive as she beat at his chest with her hands. She felt alarmingly breathless and her heart was thudding hard in her breast when she broke free at last and lay back on the pillows.

Dazedly, across Mike's shoulder she saw Driff's face appear round the edge of the door, then suddenly he was striding across the floor towards the bed. His footsteps were almost inaudible in soft-soled shoes, but some instinct must have warned Mike of his approach and he turned and looked at him over his shoulder, his brown eyes bright and daring anyone to deny him the right to be there.

'Don't you knock before you come into a lady's bedroom?' Mike asked, but Driff, despite his obvious anger, refused to rise to the bait.

Carys did not remember seeing him quite so angry before, and the glitter in his light eyes should have warned Mike that he faced formidable opposition.

'Carys is supposed to be in isolation,' Driff reminded him quietly. 'Apart from that she isn't feeling well. You'd better go, Mike.'

Carys could have told him that neither of the Shushters ever gave up until they could see they were completely routed, but she said nothing. Instead she lay back on her pillows and felt strangely content to let Driff handle things his own way. She had no doubt what the outcome would be and in her innermost heart she enjoyed the anticipation.

Mike merely shrugged and stayed where he was, sitting on the edge of her bed with one hand holding hers. 'I'm not scared off by a few cold germs,' he said, and eyed Driff with one brow raised. 'Any more than you seem to be,' he added meaningly.

Only the glittering look in Driff's eyes betrayed his temper and Carys wondered hazily how on earth he could exert such iron self-control in the face of Mike's provocation. A small pulse in his neck throbbed urgently and she watched it with hazy, fascinated eyes as he looked at Mike for a moment without speaking.

'The problem is,' he said in the same quiet voice, 'you wouldn't be content with a simple common cold, would you? The Shushters have to do everything bigger and better than everybody else, and I can imagine what your father would say if his precious son and heir developed pneumonia and there was no doctor and no hospital handy. Didn't I read somewhere one time that you're subject to bronchial trouble?'

Mike's eyes narrowed and he frowned his dislike of being reminded of something he saw as a weakness.

'Carys has got a cold in the head, for God's sake,' he argued, 'you can't think——'

'The thing is I *do* think,' Driff interrupted calmly. 'Now get to hell out of here, Mike, and stay out, do you hear me?'

The very quietness of his voice, his iron self-control, was more effective than if he had shouted and cursed, the Shushters were past masters at winning those kind of battles. As it was Mike sat for a moment longer, absorbing the situation, overawed by the sheer strength of will of his antagonist, then he raised his two hands in the air in a gesture of resignation.

'O.K., O.K.!' he said. 'I'll go, but don't think I don't see through you, Campbell—I do!'

'Good for you!' Driff answered him coolly, and held the door open for him while he got to his feet and hobbled across the room. He turned in the doorway and blew Carys a kiss as a last gesture of defiance.

'I'll see you, honey,' he told her, and hobbled out of sight towards the big living room.

Driff lingered for another second or two, his eyes searching her face, narrowed and speculative, also a little anxious, Carys thought. He came closer and stood looking down at her, then reached out with one big hand and laid it on her hot forehead. 'You've more than just a cold,' he said in a gentle voice. 'I hope you——' He stopped and shook his head slowly. 'I hope to heaven you haven't developed anything we can't deal with,' he said.

Carys could feel her heart thudding at her ribs until her head spun with its force, and her already fuzzy brain spun chaotically as she looked up at him.

'It—it's only a chill, Driff,' she told him huskily. 'It'll soon go.'

He reached for her hand, his strong fingers curled with almost desperate tightness over hers. 'I hope to God you're right,' he said. As if he suddenly recalled himself, he let go her hand and smiled down at her with his old confidence. 'You'd better get some sleep,' he told her, 'and if your boy-friend comes in again just yell or throw something—either Luan or I will hear you.'

She nodded without saying anything, but when he reached the door she called after him. 'Driff!'

He turned, his hand on the edge of the door, his light eyes darkened by the sunless gloom of the passageway. 'Hmm?'

'Thank you,' Carys whispered, and he looked surprised first, then smiled, and waved a hand before closing the door behind him.

'Any time,' he said.

CHAPTER EIGHT

IT was a relief to Carys to realise that although she felt so wretched she was suffering from nothing worse than a severe chill in her stomach. Luan had done her best to provide an invalid diet, but it was not easy because supplies were getting low. For the past six and a half weeks stocks that had been meant to feed the usual three inhabitants of the island had had to be stretched to provide for six, and the wonder was that they had fared as well as they had.

Although she was well on the way to recovery, Carys still felt quite alarmingly weak, and she wished she could do something about it, something more positive than staying in bed and recovering her strength gradually as she had been told. She had seen nothing of Mike for the past couple of days, so presumably he had decided not to risk another confrontation with their host, but she had not been in the mood to see anyone until today.

Today she felt much better and rather restless as a result. She sat up in bed looking out of the window across the clearing at the back of the house and listening to the now familiar sounds of the island—the waterfall splashing into its stone basin below the Golden Drum, the soft sound of the surf rolling up on to the white-sanded beach and the noisy chattering of the parakeets in the trees.

There were so many things special to the island

that she would miss terribly and which she would never be able to find anywhere else. It had become a very special place to her and she had an affection for the little island she had never had for any other place, a reluctance to leave it that Mike and his father would never understand. Also she was obliged to face the fact that in no more than a little over a week from now she would be forced to leave for good, no matter how she felt.

Her days in bed and the aftermath of the chill were probably responsible for her feeling so tearful, but she could do little about the sudden blurring of her vision when she thought of never seeing Driff or his island again. Driff was perhaps the main reason for her reluctance to go, but she was not yet ready to admit it, even to herself.

She sat curled up in bed with her knees hunched and her arms hugging them close to her chest. Wearing Driff's shirt gave her a gamin look that belied her years and was strangely appealing. Her face seemed to have got small in the last few days, while her eyes seemed to have grown larger and were dark-shadowed. She looked and felt utterly miserable and as far as she could see there was little she could do to remedy the situation.

She was jolted sharply out of her musings by the penetrating sound of men's voices raised in anger. Two of them belonged unmistakably to Mike and Karl Shushter, and she tilted her head to one side to listen, startled by the suddenness of the outburst. They must, she knew, be either in the big room next to hers or on the verandah, for she could hear them quite plainly and even catch an occasional word of what was being said, although not enough to make sense of it.

Another, quieter but equally firm voice reached her too, and that would be Driff, she knew. No matter how angry he was he never raised his voice, and it was so much more effective than the blustering of her late employer. The thing that troubled her most was the fact that the barely restrained antagonism of the last few weeks had actually become open hostility.

She raised her head and looked across at the door when the sound of footsteps moving softly over the matting in the passage outside drew her attention, light footsteps that she recognised as Luan's. She was tempted to call out to her, but there was a suggestion of haste in the light footsteps and a second later she heard a door close—Luan's bedroom door, she thought.

Luan's hasty retreat suggested she was involved in some way in the quarrel among the men and Carys shook her head anxiously when she began to put two and two together. There was another short, sharp altercation among the men, but it was some consolation to her that John's deep, distinctive voice was not among them. At least if John was still unaware of Mike's fancy for his young wife, the position was not irreversible. Driff could perhaps impress upon Mike the foolhardiness of such a liaison.

But Mike, it seemed a few moments later, was not convinced and his angry voice could be heard quite distinctly shouting defiance. 'It's none of your business, Campbell, keep out of it!' His gait was still distinguishably uneven, thanks to his injured ankle, and seconds later Carys heard him thumping across the wooden floor of the verandah. He was closely followed by the heavier and even more determined tread that betrayed his father, and then it was quiet.

Breathless with anxiety in the silence that followed, Carys listened intently but heard nothing for several seconds. Then once more footsteps whispered over the rush matting outside her door and she knew without a doubt that it must be Driff. She hesitated only briefly, then called out to him.

'Driff?'

Her voice was sharp with anxiety and her heart was thudding heavily in her breast while she watched the bedroom door and waited to see if he would reply to her call. Then the door opened, just a fraction, and he looked in, a look on his face that suggested he was not quite sure if she had called him or not.

Carys looked small and pale curled up in the bed. His shirt was many sizes too big for her and its bulk enveloped her slim body in shapeless folds, its collar turned up to frame her face and the front of it opened part way to let the cool air to her skin. Driff stood looking across from the doorway for several seconds before he eventually came further into the room.

Then he came and stood beside the bed, studying her again with a curiously glittering look that troubled her. 'Driff——' She licked her dry lips anxiously. 'I—I thought I heard voices,' she ventured, and his wide mouth curved into a harsh caricature of itself.

'You heard a fight,' he said flatly, 'and you're

curious!'

His harshness hurt as well as startled her, and Carys looked up at him anxiously. 'I—I was worried in case——'

'You don't have to worry,' he interrupted shortly, 'no one got hurt, though it's a miracle I didn't lash out, injury or not!'

Carys blinked, disturbed by the violence of his anger. 'I—I think I can guess what—who caused it,' she told him, and for a moment he looked at her steadily, a glitter in his eyes that she did not like at all.

'You probably can,' he said after a few seconds. 'After all, I guess you know him pretty well, don't you?'

'Mike?' His implication had been unmistakable and Carys flinched from it. 'Not as well as you're implying,' she told him in a small voice. 'I've told you that before, Driff.'

'I've been told a lot of things before,' Driff told her harshly. 'The problem is, who do I believe? He's still claiming that once he can get you away from here you'll do as he says you will and marry him—that being here changed your mind about him. You say you won't marry him and swear you never intended to!'

'I didn't and I still don't!' Carys declared.

It seemed so important to convince him, and she looked up at him anxiously. He could disturb her as no man ever had before, and she was beginning to recognise that the more she saw of him the more she hated the idea of leaving with Mike and his father when the boat came. She felt she knew him so completely, and yet there always seemed to be new facets to his character to surprise her.

His fair hair was damp and looked darker than usual and she assumed he had been swimming, and the light slacks and shirt he wore fitted him closely, emphasising his long muscular legs and the broad chest his carelessly buttoned shirt revealed.

His strong bare arms tanned by the island sun and the big brown hands that she knew could be so gentle both glistened with the residue of salt water. There was an aura of vigorous, masculine aggression about him that stirred her emotions into chaos as he stood beside her, and she wanted to reach out and touch him with an urgency that startled her.

'O.K., I believe you!' His mouth smiled crookedly and he was shaking his head, as if he had difficulty in understanding his own reasons. 'I guess because I want to,' he added, half under his breath. 'Though why in hell I should care one way or the other is beyond me!'

Carys said nothing for a moment. It was difficult to think coherently when he was standing so close and she was so easily affected by him. He had been arguing with Mike, but she was not absolutely sure whether it was simply an inherent dislike of Mike that had caused the quarrel or whether, as she suspected, Mike had been misbehaving with Luan again.

'You—you were arguing with Mike about——' She bit her lip anxiously, finding it difficult to put into words. It occurred to her too late that he had misinterpreted her words when one fair brow arched swiftly and he shook his head.

'Disappointing as it might be,' he told her with a hint of cynicism, 'we weren't arguing about you.'

'Oh, of course you weren't!' Carys denied hastily. 'I never for a moment thought you were! I heard Luan just now and I thought——'

'You thought right!' Driff said shortly. 'Though it need not concern you, if you really *don't* intend marrying him!'

Carys shook her head. 'It concerns me because— well, because we're intruders and—and I like John and Luan very much.' If only Mike could have controlled his boredom for just a little longer, they need not have aroused even more resentment in their unwilling host. 'I—I'm sorry,' she said, not knowing quite what else to say that would convey how she felt.

'What for?' Driff asked quietly. 'It isn't your fault he wants to have his cake and eat it too, is it?'

'No—no, of course not,' Carys said in a small anxious voice.

'Then don't apologise for him!' He sounded as if he disliked her doing that almost as much as he did Mike's behaviour with Luan. He ran one big hand through his blond hair in a gesture of impatient helplessness. 'God in heaven,' he breathed earnestly, 'I'll be glad when you three are on that boat and heading out of here!'

'Yes, of course you will.' It hurt to hear him so ready to discard her in the same breath with Mike and his father, and she sat with her eyes downcast, looking at her hands and feeling more despondent than before he came in. The tears that had threatened her before now formed an obscuring mist in her eyes and she did her best to hold them back.

'Surely *you'll* be glad to get back to more familiar surroundings,' he suggested, and Carys glanced at him from the corners of her eyes, not daring to look at him directly.

His hands hung at his sides and she could see that they were curled, as her own were, the long fingers tensed but not clenched, and there was an air of tautness about him that made her watch him uneasily. 'No, I won't! I like it here, Driff,' she reminded him, 'for the same reasons you do.'

'Yes, of course you do.' He sounded as if it was something he had forgotten until she reminded him, and once again she flinched from the hurt he unthinkingly inflicted on her.

Her heart was pounding desperately hard and she felt small and uncertain, searching for something, some reason for her not to leave the island when the others did. Her need to stay on was almost more than she could bear and again she wanted to reach out and touch him, to feel the warm, tanned skin under her fingertips.

'Driff——' She licked her lips nervously, and he waited silently, watching her with those steady, disturbing eyes. 'If you—I mean, I don't work for Karl Shushter any more, and if you—if you needed someone to take notes—to type out——'

'No, honey!' He was shaking his head firmly, as if he was not even going to consider the idea. 'Definitely not!'

Carys felt her stomach curling with embarrassment when she realised her mistake. He was probably putting her into the same category as the mysterious Elizabeth he had told her about, who had followed him to his island and promptly been sent back again —leaving behind a pair of her shoes and an expensive antique ring.

'Women and work don't mix, honey,' he told her gently, so infinitely gentle that it played havoc with her self-control, 'not for me they don't. I couldn't concentrate with you sitting there pounding the type-writer.'

It was bitterly disappointing to hear him so rigidly adamant, but really it was no more than she should have expected. Just the same she swallowed hastily when she saw her only excuse for staying on so easily dismissed. 'No,' she said, 'of course not. I—I just thought——'

'I know you did, Carys.' He reached out with one hand and lightly touched her cheek. 'But it wouldn't work, believe me. As soon as you and the Shushters have gone I have to make up for lost time, and having you stay on wouldn't help at all.'

'No—no, I know—I'm sorry.'

It was so hard to accept it calmly and matter-of-factly, and she wished now that he would go and leave her alone, for she felt sure she was going to cry. Not because he had refused to let her work for him, she had not really expected him to change his rules to accommodate her, but because he was so determined to see her gone with the others, and she wanted so much to stay near him.

'You don't have to apologise, for heaven's sake,' he told her with a smile that banished the last of his earlier temper. 'You weren't to know how uncivilised I get when I'm working. I'd scare the living daylights out of any woman in that situation—believe me, Karl Shushter's got nothing on me for sheer brute tyranny!' He touched her cheek again lightly. 'You go back home and find some nice elderly business exec to work for, honey—you'll be much better off!'

Carys knew she was not going to be able to hold back the tears for much longer, they already filled her eyes and threatened to roll down her cheeks at any minute and give the game away. 'I wish you'd go now,' she whispered huskily. 'I—I know I'm going to make an idiot of myself and cry, and I don't—I don't want you feeling sorry for me!'

'Oh, Carys!' He dropped on to the edge of the bed facing her and his arms reached out for her, drawing her close to him, one big hand soothingly gentle on her head while the other held her against his chest. 'Don't cry, honey, please!'

Carys turned her face to the smooth softness of his shirt, conscious of the warm tanned skin through its thin texture, and closed her eyes. Every nerve in her body cried out for him and in that moment she would have given anything to be allowed to stay with him. As she clung to him tightly, her emotions responded with a violence that startled her and she was more shiveringly aware of the strong masculine arms that enfolded her than she had ever been before. Of the tangy combination of salt water mingled with the warmth of his body, the slight dampness it still retained after his swim.

A light kiss on her forehead brought her to a sense of reality again, for it reminded her that his embrace had been meant to console her, not to suggest anything more meaningful. She clung to her dream for a moment longer, then stirred in his arms without looking up. 'I—I like it here so much,' she said, trying to explain in a voice that was muffled against his chest. 'I—I thought if I could—I was wrong, Driff, I know it's not possible.'

'Not if I want to get any work done,' Driff murmured beside her ear, and laughed softly. 'And you know I wouldn't!'

'I know.' She closed her eyes again and tried to pretend it was not going to end any second now. 'I'm —I'm sorry if I embarrassed you by being such a— a cry-baby.'

'You didn't, and you aren't,' Driff assured her, his lips pressed briefly against her forehead. 'You're feeling rotten after being sick for several days, and you wanted a shoulder to cry on—so who's going to blame you for that?'

Carys raised her head at last and looked at him with eyes that still bore traces of tears. Her hands were spread over his white shirt and through it the shadowy darkness of his body pulsed warmly under her fingertips. 'We really have caused you a lot of trouble one way and another, haven't we?' she asked in a small husky voice.

Driff made no attempt to deny it, but pulled a face and crooked his mouth into a smile that crinkled his eyes. 'I guess you have,' he agreed, and laughed when she looked at him reproachfully.

'Well, in another few days you'll be rid of us,' Carys said. 'Then you can go back to work and forget all about us!'

Driff looked at her for a long moment without saying anything and Carys felt her heart pounding anxiously as she looked up and met the glistening look in his light eyes. 'Maybe,' he said quietly. He looked as if he might have said more, but someone somewhere closed a door and he shook his head as if to clear it. 'Unless somebody else dumps another plane into the Pacific!' he added with a rueful smile.

'Or another girl-friend stows away on your supply ship,' Carys retorted, and he laughed, looking down at her steadily.

'Or that,' he agreed quietly.

Carys got up the following day because she felt that perhaps her reappearance might help to distract Mike from his pursuit of Luan, although she did not look forward to having him renew his efforts to get her to marry him. Luan was quite obviously glad to see her at the breakfast table, but Carys noticed that she quite pointedly ignored Mike.

Mike made a great deal of fuss and saw her seated with a show of concern that seemed to surprise Driff if his expression was anything to judge by. Thwarted in his own efforts to see her seated, he sat down at the end of the table and looked down at her with a raised brow and a hint of smile that brought swift colour to her cheeks.

She looked pale-faced and felt alarmingly shaky

after nearly a week in bed, but it was good to be up and about again and sharing her meals with the rest of them. Karl Shushter did not actually enquire after her health, but he did nod across to her when she sat down, and murmured a brief good morning.

After breakfast Mike had plans for them to go down to the beach together, plans that Carys did not feel inclined to fall in with as easily as he obviously expected her to. For one thing she felt annoyed with him still about his attitude towards Luan. It was obvious that he had simply seen her as someone to amuse himself with while Carys was unavailable, for he had not even spoken to her this morning.

Carys preferred to stay nearer the house where they were unlikely to be completely alone for very long, and she would be spared the necessity of turning him down yet again. Mike agreed to stay with her, though only grudgingly she was left in no doubt, and he perched himself on a stool beside her while she sat in the big wickerwork chair.

As she had hoped, they were not entirely alone, for Karl Shushter sat on the verandah step, leaning against the rail support and gazing morosely across at the ocean. Once or twice Mike glanced across at him uneasily, as if he found his presence inhibiting, then suddenly he looked up at Carys and frowned, his mouth hinting at sulkiness.

'What's bothering you, honey?' he asked. 'You seem kind of—off, somehow.'

Carys too glanced across at Karl Shushter before she answered, wondering how much of their conversation would be audible to him. 'Are you surprised

I'm—off, as you call it?' she asked. 'When you've been pestering Luan again!'

Mike looked relieved, she thought, as if he could easily talk his way out of that. He laughed and took her hand in his, shaking his head as he looked up at her with bright challenging eyes. 'Are you jealous, sweetheart?' he asked, only half joking. 'Are you actually jealous of Campbell's little serving wench?'

Carys angled her chin. It was difficult not to lose her temper with him when he was being so offhand about something that could have been very serious for Luan and John. 'No, Mike, I'm not jealous,' she told him, so coolly that she surprised even herself. 'But Luan isn't a serving wench, she's a friend, and I don't like you going out of your way to make trouble for her just to amuse yourself! I happen to like her and John too, I don't want to see either of them hurt.'

'Then maybe we should all change partners!' Mike suggested acidly. 'You take John Kanaka and I'll take Luan!'

He disliked being criticised as much as he disliked being stopped from doing something he wanted to do, and his good-looking features were flushed dark pink as he stared ahead of him, his hands clenched tightly. It would be hopeless to try and reason with him, no doubt Driff had already tried that and failed, hence the quarrel yesterday.

Carys fought with a desire to turn round on him and tell him exactly what she thought of him but, knowing how uncomfortable further quarrels could make the remainder of their stay, she refrained. Instead she managed to keep her voice fairly steady and controlled.

'You're not being very fair, Mike,' she told him. 'Not only to John and Luan but to the rest of us as well. There's so little time left now and it would make things so much easier if we could get through the next week without quarrelling.'

'Oh, spare me the lecture!' Mike begged impatiently. 'I had enough of that yesterday from Campbell and Pop!'

Carys, taken completely by surprise, blinked at him unbelievingly. 'Your—your father?' she asked, and glanced across at Karl Shushter's sharply handsome profile, like chiselled granite against the soft purple blossom of the bougainvillea.

'Can you figure it?' Mike asked. 'He sided with Campbell and sailed into me for making time with Luan!'

It was hard to believe initially, Carys had to admit, and yet in some curious way it was typical of Karl Shushter. He was a harsh taskmaster to his thousands of employees, and his business tactics were sometimes quite close to being crooked, but he was not a promiscuous man and he had legally married all three of the women in his life.

There were also the fact that he would probably dislike seeing his son make a fool of himself with one of the servants he had made it so obvious he despised. If he did he would not have hesitated to say so, whether Mike liked it or not. No matter what his motives in supporting Driff, it was the first time since she had known him that Carys found herself in agreement with anything he did.

'I don't think I'm really surprised,' she told Mike, and he looked at her and frowned, obviously disliking her answer.

'Well, I was!' he admitted. He sat morosely silent for some time while Carys looked across at Karl Shushter again and wondered how she could have been in close contact with a man day after day for nearly eight months and still not really know him. Then Mike looked up at her again suddenly, his eyes narrowed. 'How did you know about the fight yesterday?' he asked, and Carys shrugged.

'I heard you quarrelling,' she told him. 'You were making so much noise I could almost hear what you were saying.'

'You heard me having it out with Campbell,' Mike said, 'but how did you know it was about Luan? It might have been about you!'

'It wasn't, Mike, it was about Luan!'

She realised that she might be on thin ice when she saw his look, and again glanced across at Karl Shushter, almost glad to have him there although she could not have said why. 'You're so sure,' Mike said in a flatly soft voice, his brown eyes glinting. 'How come you're so sure, Carys? Did Luan tell you? Did she come crying to you because Campbell caught us together—trying to put all the blame on me?'

'No, of course she didn't!' Carys denied. 'She was upset and she went straight to her room, I heard her!'

'Then somebody else took the trouble to come and tell you that I'd stepped out of line,' Mike said, his eyes narrowed, 'and I don't have to guess who *that* was! Holy smoke—he just couldn't wait to tell you what a no-good I am, could he?'

'Mike, you're——'

'I'm seeing you for what you are, sweetheart!' Mike interrupted harshly. 'There's been a whole lot of accusations flying around about *my* character, but so far nobody's looked too close at yours, have they? I came to visit you and got thrown out on my ear, but Campbell—oh no! He gets the welcome mat! I guess you went for his reputation—he's older than me and he's been around more!'

'Mike, stop it!' Carys's hands were curled tightly and she felt so angry she could have struck him. Those few moments with Driff had been very precious to her and now he was doing his best to reduce it to something sly and sordid. She managed to control her voice to some extent, but it still sounded a little unsteady. 'I—I heard Driff in the passage outside my room,' she told him, 'and I called him in—I wanted to know what had happened.'

'So you say!'

Carys got to her feet. Not even to keep the peace would she stay and listen to him making the kind of suggestions he was, and as she got up so did he, his brown eyes glittering angrily. From the corner of her eye she saw that Karl Shushter had left his seat on the verandah step and was coming across to join them, soft-footed on the board floor. Expecting a combined assault, she steeled herself to face them.

Standing beside his son, Karl Shushter looked at him steadily for a moment, then he shook his head slowly. 'Don't make any more of a fool of yourself, Mike,' he said quietly. 'Why don't you quit while you're ahead?'

Mike turned on him, a hint of desperation in his manner that almost had Carys feeling sorry for him. He was so used to the unquestioning support of his father that he would feel betrayed, having him speak against him twice in as many days. 'Are you telling me to stay away from Carys too?' he asked in a flat voice, and his father looked for a second at Carys, his hard grey eyes narrowed and shrewd.

'I'm telling you not to chase a lost cause, son,' he said. 'If this girl was on the make she'd have snapped you up a couple of months ago when you first asked her. If she's making a play for Campbell instead you can bet your last dollar she's stuck on the guy himself —you could buy him out as a job lot and still get change! Leave it, son, it's a lost cause!'

There was something oddly touching about the short and rather crude speech, and Carys saw the logic of it, although by the look on his face Mike did not, as yet. He looked at his father and then at Carys, and she reached out impulsively and put a hand on his arm. It was more difficult than it had ever been before, but she felt so much more sorry for him than she had other times when she had told him.

'I'm sorry, Mike,' she said softly, 'but I've said no so often and you haven't believed I meant it—perhaps now that your father's told you you'll see that I do mean it.'

Mike said nothing, he simply looked utterly dejected and Carys stood between the two of them feeling very small and intrusive. Between them Mike and his father could, as Karl Shushter had hinted, buy her, Driff and his island and still have change—and yet for all that they were losers in other, more intimate matters, and she thought Karl Shushter knew it. For Mike the disillusionment was only just beginning.

CHAPTER NINE

CARYS looked across the glittering, shimmering surface of the ocean and hugged her knees close to her breast, her eyes hazy with preoccupation. At any time now Driff's yacht, *Water Bird*, would come into sight on the horizon and she would know for sure that it was all over—that she would never see either Driff or Isleta del Tambor Dorado again.

A week ago the idea of leaving had seemed unbearable; now it was heartbreaking and she ached with the hopelessness of loving a man like Driff Campbell, a man who was dedicated to his work and left room in his life for only the most casual affairs.

Carys had not been alone with him again since that controversial visit to her bedroom a week ago, but she knew for certain that she loved him, no matter how unaffected he remained. All the week she had looked for some sign of his relenting his hard and fast rule about visitors, but so far she had seen nothing to suggest it, although she clung to her hopes until the very last minute.

Mike had been quiet, even restrained, all week, but his reasons for being aloof had nothing to do with a reluctance to leave the island, she knew, for he made no secret of the fact that he could not wait to get away. He saw the island as the basis for his present frustration and unhappiness and did not attempt to disguise it.

He said nothing to Driff, except what politeness obliged him to, and little to Carys, and sometimes she felt a little guilty about seeing him so morose and unhappy and would have liked to do something about it. But she knew that if she did it would inevitably lead up to a situation that she did not feel up to coping with at the moment.

Water Bird was to take them back to Honolulu and from there Carys would have to make her own arrangements. She was no longer in the employ of Karl Shushter, so she could either return to England or try to find herself another job in Hawaii. With no family ties to influence her her movements depended entirely upon her own inclinations.

The temptation to stay in Hawaii, she frankly admitted to herself, was largely because she knew that Driff had a house there too, but she also liked living in the islands, so there was a good deal in favour of her staying. Her social life would probably be on a slightly different scale from what she had enjoyed with Mike, but there was always plenty to do, and the chance that one day she might bump into Driff when he was visiting Honolulu again.

'Carys.'

She looked up swiftly, startled out of her daydream by John Kanaka's quiet friendly voice. He stood smiling down at her, but his smile was tentative and a little anxious, and Carys suspected he knew as well as Luan did why she did not want to leave. Neither of them had said a word, but she sensed their sympathy and, in a way, appreciated it. The look in John's dark eyes was almost more disturbing than her own thoughts had been and she hated feeling so vulnerable.

'Hello, John!' She smiled, determinedly cheerful. 'It isn't lunch time already, surely, is it?'

'Not yet,' John said, and hesitated a moment. 'The yacht's in sight, Carys—I've just spotted her from the drum.'

'Oh! Oh, I see—thank you.' She managed another smile somehow, though heaven knew how when her heart seemed to have stopped, and she felt suddenly cold and numb. 'Does Driff know?' she asked, and he shook his head.

'Not yet, honey,' he told her, his voice gentle. 'I came to let you know first.'

'Thank you.' He stood looking down at her for a second, as if he was uncertain if he should leave her or not, and Carys stood the silence as long as she could, then she looked up and shook her head, her mouth smiling despite the dark unhappiness in her eyes. 'I never did get to the top and actually see the Drum close to, or that marvellous view from up there, did I?' she asked, and laughed shakily. 'I don't suppose I ever will now.'

John's dark eyes pitied her unhappiness and were almost her undoing. 'You want me to take you up there now?' he asked. 'You can see *Water Bird* pretty good from up there.'

'Is she that close?' Carys looked up at him anxiously, and he nodded his head.

'About two hours out, I guess,' he told her. 'Maybe a little more.'

'Two hours!'

Carys hugged her knees more tightly to her and tried to imagine herself calmly walking on board the *Water Bird*, then sailing out of Driff's life for good. It wasn't easy and the fact would, she knew, be much harder than the anticipation, but it had to be done and she was helpless to change anything. Helpless to do anything about Driff's adamant insistence on isolation—about his rule of no females other than Luan on his island.

'About two hours,' John agreed, and once more brought her sharply out of a day-dream. 'She'll be here for about two days maybe, before she goes back.'

'Taking the unwelcome visitors with her!' Carys said, and laughed without humour. 'What a relief that will be to everybody!'

'Not you,' John denied, quietly assured. 'You were never unwelcome, Carys, we liked having you here—me and Luan.'

'But not Driff!' Carys remarked bitterly. 'He can't wait to be rid of us!'

John was shaking his head firmly, and there was a glint in his dark eyes that somehow reminded her of Driff. 'You don't know him,' he argued, staunchly loyal to Driff as always. 'He's a strong man, single-minded maybe, but not untouchable!'

'Isn't he?'

John was shaking his head. 'You should know, honey,' he told her. 'You've given him a hard time—you got to him like nobody ever did before.'

It was simply wishful thinking, Carys told herself, to allow herself to believe him, but John sounded so certain he was right and he probably knew him better than anyone else. 'I don't—I don't quite believe that,' she said in a small unsteady voice. 'He's still glad to see me go, he told me so. No, I can't believe I ever got near him, John—not Driff.'

'It's true,' John insisted. 'Believe me, I know him! But he'll fight to keep his island the way he planned it, no matter what happens. Like I said, he's a strong man and he don't give in easy.'

'Oh, John——' She shook her head, refusing to grasp even the smallest crumb of hope. 'Don't think I haven't tried to make him change,' she said. 'I even asked him if he'd take me on as his secretary, but he gave me a firm no almost before I asked the question!'

'He would,' said John, nodding his head. 'He's kind of hard to move once he's dug in his heels, and this island means a lot to him, he won't give up easy, not all it means to him—the peace and quiet, time to work.'

'I know.'

She looked very small and unhappy sitting there and John stood looking at her for a second before he spoke again, as if there was something on his mind. 'I haven't told anybody else yet that the boat's coming,' he told her. 'Would you like I should take you up to see the drum, Carys, before I let the others know?'

Carys hesitated, anxious and uncertain, but she gave him her hands so that he could help her to her feet, and his handsome brown face was thoughtful as he studied her, waiting for her answer. 'I'd like to go up there just once before I go,' Carys said, and brushed sand from her dress with hands that were oddly clumsy suddenly. 'But I'd like to go alone, John, by the easy way from the back.'

John looked doubtful. He frowned and glanced at the house, as if he expected Driff to appear at any moment and take the situation out of his hands. 'I don't think Driff would like it,' he warned, but Carys smiled and shook her head.

'Oh, I don't think he'd mind now,' she told him. 'If I do fall and hurt myself I won't be a bother to him for very long, the boat will be here in a couple of hours to ship me out to the nearest doctor!'

John still hesitated, but eventually, with a shrug of his broad shoulders, he gave in. 'O.K., if that's how you want it,' he told her. 'But please be careful, Carys, we'd hate it if anything happened to you— and so would Driff, I know.'

'So would I,' Carys assured him. 'Don't worry, John, I'll be very careful, but I must see that view, just once.'

He walked with her as far as the house, then left her with a final admonishment to be careful, presumably on his way to inform Driff and the Shushters that *Water Bird* was in sight and relief was imminent. Driff would be delighted to get the news, Carys thought bitterly as she made her way round to the back of the house, and so would Mike and his father.

Her mind preoccupied with how little time she had left, Carys made her way carefully up the scrub-covered incline and found it a much more gradual access to the Drum than the steep climb she had attempted before via the rocks that flanked the waterfall. It took her quite a lot longer going that way, but it involved much less effort and was less hazardous, the more dense scrub offering better holds than bare rock.

The scrub grew even more dense as she got nearer to the top, then ended abruptly, so that she came upon the huge yellow boulder unexpectedly. As it was so high up the wind was quite fresh and she could hear the rushing sound of the water as it gushed from the cleft in the rock, shimmering like rainbows in the sun.

There was a clearing around the Drum itself and its golden yellow bulk loomed against the clear blue sky like a great nugget. It was, Carys decided as she climbed the last few breathless yards, even more awe-inspiring from close quarters than from below, though much less easily distinguishable as a drum shape. Up here it was simply a huge boulder, impressive but not endowed with any discernible shape.

Turning to look across at the view she had come to see, Carys drew an audible breath at its magnificence. She could have been on the top of the world, she seemed so high up, and the very endlessness of it was over-awing, for the horizon was vast in every direction.

Stretched out before her, seemingly into eternity, the blue Pacific rolled and rippled in the sun with not a sign of the white crests that had whipped across its surface the last time she had taken such an elevated view of it. Then, right on the horizon, she saw the hazy form of a boat, its size indeterminate at the moment because of the distance—*Water Bird* making her way to the island, coming to take her away from the Isle of the Golden Drum and from Driff.

As she stood and looked at it, drawn like a hazy white dot on the blue horizon, her eyes filled with tears that blurred her vision and hid it from sight. Reminded again of her imminent departure, she turned away and laid her hot forehead against the cool yellow rock, her eyes closed. It could do no good to cry, it would change nothing, but the need to do so was irresistible.

It was as she raised her head that she saw Driff step out from behind the Drum itself and gasped, instinctively taking a half step backwards as she stared at him. Driff stood looking at her without speaking—a steady, disturbing look that shivered through her like a warning, and curled her hands into tight little fists at her side.

'Driff?' Her mouth felt dry and her head was spinning with the effect of her violently beating heart as she looked at him. 'How—how did you get here before me?'

She knew the answer, of course, even before he spoke. He had taken the steeper, quicker way up, but with what purpose in mind? she wondered. Was he really concerned that she might come to some harm up there alone, as she had the last time she had ventured the climb on her own?

'I took a short cut,' he told her with a lightness that was belied by the deep, serious look in his light blue eyes. They were narrowed against the glare of the sun and reminded her of the first time she had seen him, rowing them away from the wreckage of the plane—

two whole months ago. 'I told you never to come up here alone,' he reminded her. 'But you never did mind me, did you, Carys?'

Carys found it hard to think coherently while he stood there looking at her like that and she could feel her heart beating away urgently against her ribs, as if in panic. The last time they had been alone together he had taken her into his arms and comforted her, but she prayed desperately that he was not going to do that now. She could not have borne being in his arms when he was merely comforting her—now that she needed so much more from him.

Her whole being cried out for him, and she shivered, despite the hot sun. 'I—I hardly thought it would matter to you now,' she said, and her voice sounded small and husky with emotion.

His light blue eyes watched her closely and she found their scrutiny almost unbearable. With one hand on the solid bulk of the Golden Drum she stood on legs that suddenly felt alarmingly weak and unsteady, trying to control the rapid and breathtaking urgency of her heartbeat.

'Do you think I don't care if you get hurt?' he asked, and something in his voice quickened her pulse even more. A roughness, a hint of emotions held in restraint that stirred an urgent response in her, although she still did not look at him.

Instead she looked down at her feet and at the pale blue sandals left behind by his previous uninvited visitor. 'It wouldn't matter so much to you now, would it?' she said. 'Your yacht's on its way and I'll —we'll be gone in a few hours—you won't have to be bothered with us any more.'

It was not easy to speak about it as if it was simply a matter of course now, and she wished with all her heart that she had not told John of her intention to climb up to the Drum before she left. She should have known he would tell Driff where she'd gone, as she should have known that Driff would come for her himself instead of sending John. Perhaps, she realised with sudden insight, that was really why she had come—in the hope that Driff would follow her.

'You still don't want to go?' he asked, and Carys shook her head, almost before the words were out of his mouth, a brief flutter of hope stirring in her heart when she looked at him.

'You *know* I don't want to go!' she whispered. 'I don't want to leave here, and I don't want to——' She bit her lip anxiously, holding back the hurt that gnawed at her so relentlessly. It was bad enough that he should see her crying like a baby because she had to leave the island—she could not bear his pity if he knew the real reason behind the wanting to stay.

As she stood with her head bowed, her long hair fell forward and partially hid her face, but through the haze of tears that clouded her vision she could see the lean straightness of his body and the hands that hung now at his sides, curled as if he held himself in check. That strong, masculine force he emanated reached out and enveloped her, playing havoc with her emotions and her resistance.

'Carys!'

He spoke her name barely above a whisper and took the few steps needed to bring him into contact with her—a swift, hard contact that burned her like fire as he folded his arms about her and drew her close against him. Clinging to him tightly, she buried her face against the broad warm comfort of his chest, not caring for the moment what his reason was for holding her—it was enough that she was in his arms.

The familiar scent of his after-shave mingled with the warmth of his body and the tangy freshness of salt water enveloped her completely and she closed her eyes, shutting out everything but the beloved, familiar touch of his body. 'Don't send me away!' she whispered, her voice muffled against his shirt. 'Please, Driff, don't send me away!'

He said nothing for a moment, but his hands soothed her gently, his mouth touching lightly on her forehead and the small pulse beside her ear. 'Carys, sweetheart!' His voice was deep and soft as he brushed aside the thick dark hair from her neck and bent his head to kiss her throat. 'Do you think I *want* you to go?'

'I—I don't know!' She clung to him more tightly, her hands spread on his back, feeling the warm, tanned smoothness of his skin through the thin shirt he wore.

'You're a distraction, sweetheart,' he told her, his voice muffled against the softness of her neck. 'You can play havoc with my working schedule if I let you stay.'

'Can I?' Carys raised her head at last and looked at him with bright, glowing grey eyes. Searching his face, the familiar strong features that were now so incredibly dear to her, she felt a fluttering of hope in her heart that filled her with a sudden intense excitement.

His arms held her tight against the firm hardness of his body and he looked down at her with such a look in his eyes that she felt herself trembling. 'Don't you know it?' he asked softly.

It seemed easier suddenly to meet his gaze, and she tipped back her head, shaking back the long hair and looking at him with an exciting new confidence. Her heart was beating so hard and fast it made her head spin and her fingers curved, digging into his firm flesh. 'Then won't you let me stay?' she asked, huskily breathless but no longer afraid of his answer.

Driff laughed softly, shaking his head at her. 'You know the answer to that well enough too,' he told her. 'Why else do you suppose I came up here to find you?'

'Driff——'

Whatever she had been going to say was forgotten the moment his mouth touched hers, and she was pulled so close to him that they might almost have been one form standing up there on the yellow rock. Her lips parted under the fierceness of his kiss and the tingling, sensual pressure of his body bound her slenderness to him. His strong fingers moved the soft hair from her neck and he pressed his lips to the warm, scented skin, then pushing aside the thin cotton dress he kissed the smoothness of her shoulders and her throat.

Lifting his head at last, he looked down at her with his light eyes bright and glittering with a depth of passion that left her breathless. Then the brown face crinkled into a smile and he shook his head slowly, touching her lips lightly with his between each word. 'I knew you'd get into my blood the very first time I saw you,' he said, his voice shivering huskily. 'I *can't* let you go back with the *Water Bird*, my sweetheart, I'm crazy about you and if you leave me I'll never write again!'

Carys smiled, a deep glow in her grey eyes that made them look dark and smoky as she looked up at him. 'I don't want to leave you,' she reminded him. 'I love you.'

'Then marry me!' The light eyes crinkled at their corners and Carys knew she would never again in her life know a moment quite like this. 'Will you, my darling?'

Her answer was to lift her face to him again and with her arms around his neck she pulled his head down to her while he touched her mouth with his, lightly at first and then with an urgency that took her breath away, and she never gave another thought to the boat that still moved slowly and inexorably towards the island—it no longer mattered.

THE
OMNIBUS
A GREAT IDEA FROM HARLEQUIN

NOW ON SALE AT YOUR FAVORITE BOOKSTORE

READ ON FOR EXCITING DETAILS ...

Essie Summers

Bride in Flight (#933)

. . . begins on the eve of Kirsty's wedding, when a
strange telephone call changes her life. Blindly,
instinctively, Kirsty runs—but even New Zealand isn't
far enough to avoid the complications that follow!

Postscript to Yesterday (#1119)

. . . Nicola was dirty, exasperated and a little bit
frightened. After her amateur mechanics on the car she
was in no shape to meet any man, let alone Forbes
Westerfield. He was the man who had told her not to
come.

Meet on My Gound (#1326)

. . . is the story of two people in love, separated by pride.
Alastair Campbell had money and position—Sarah
Macdonald was a girl with pride. But pride was little
comfort to her after she'd let Alastair go!

Jean S. MacLeod

The Wolf of Heimra (#990)

. . . Fenella knew that in spite of her love for the island,
she had no claim on Heimra yet—until an heir was born.
They were so sure of themselves, these MacKails; they
expected everything to come their way.

Summer Island (#1314)

. . . Cathie's return to Loch Arden was traumatic. She
knew she was clinging to the past, not wanting to let it
go. But change was something you thought of happening in other places–never in your own beloved glen.

Slave of the Wind (#1339)

. . . Lesley's pleasure at coming home and meeting the
handsome stranger quickly changed to dismay when
she discovered that he was Maxwell Croy—the man
whose family once owned her home. And Maxwell was
determined to get it back again.

HARLEQUIN OMNIBUS

A Jumbo Read !!!

Eleanor Farnes

The Red Cliffs (#975)

. . . Alison had no particular interest in the old Devonshire cottage she had inherited; her work was in London. But when the overbearing Neil Edgerton wanted to buy it, she was faced with a sudden decision.

The Flight of the Swan (#1280)

. . . It took six months for Philippa Northern to change her life—to shed her mid-Victorian upbringing, develop her hidden self and find the happiness in living she had never before known. Then a jealous woman threatened to destroy everything!

Sister of the Housemaster (#1335)

. . . Ingrid hadn't met her sister-in-law's famous brother Patrick and didn't want to. She thought he'd be just as disagreeable as Sylvia. When they did meet, she knew she was wrong, though at first she wouldn't admit it!

Mary Burchell

The Heart Cannot Forget (#1003)

. . . Deepdene Estate should rightfully be inherited by Antonia's cousin Giles, but for some mysterious reason, he had been cast out. While living there, Antonia slowly uncovers fragments of the mystery, but everything that she learns is directly linked with the woman Giles plans to marry!

Ward of Lucifer (#1165)

. . . It was a struggle from the start. Norma knew exactly what she wanted, but Justin used her to further his own interests. He found, almost too late, that her happiness meant more to him than his own.

A Home for Joy (#1330)

. . . After her father's death, Joy accepted the kind offer of a home with her aunt and uncle and cousins. Only later did she discover that the offer was not as kind as it had seemed: there were certain strings attached.

HARLEQUIN OMNIBUS

A Jumbo Read!!

Susan Barrie

Marry a Stranger (#1034)
. . . If she lived to be a hundred, Stacey knew she'd never be more violently in love than she was at this moment. But Edouard had told her bluntly that he would never fall in love with her!

Rose in the Bud (#1168)
. . . One thing Cathleen learned in Venice: it was very important to be cautious about a man who was a stranger and inhabited a world unfamiliar to her. The more charm he possessed, the more wary she should be!

The Marriage Wheel (#1311)
. . . Admittedly the job was unusual—lady chauffeur to Humphrey Lestrode; and admittedly Humphrey was high-handed and arrogant. Nevertheless Frederica was enjoying her work at Farthing Hall. Then along came her mother and beautiful sister, Rosaleen, to upset everything.

Violet Winspear

Beloved Tyrant (#1032)
. . . Monterey was a beautiful place in which to recuperate. Lyn's job was interesting. Everything, in fact, would have been perfect, Lyn Gilmore thought, if it hadn't been for the hateful Rick Corderas. But he made her feel alive again!

Court of the Veils (#1267)
. . . In the lush plantation on the edge of the Sahara, Roslyn Brant tried very hard to remember her fiancé and her past. But the bitter, disillusioned Duane Hunter refused to believe that she was ever engaged to his cousin, Armand.

Palace of the Peacocks (#1318)
. . . Suddenly the island, this exotic place that so recently had given her sanctuary, seemed an unlucky place rather than a magical one. She must get away from the cold palace and its ghost—and especially from Ryk van Helden.

Harlequin Reader Service

ORDER FORM

MAIL COUPON TO ➡ Harlequin Reader Service,
M.P.O. Box 707,
Niagara Falls, New York 14302.

Canadian SEND Residents TO: ➡ Harlequin Reader Service,
Stratford, Ont. N5A 6W4

Harlequin Omnibus

OTHER AUTHORS AVAILABLE

Please check volumes requested:

☐ Essie Summers 1   ☐ Anne Weale   ☐ Amanda Doyle
☐ Jean S. MacLeod   ☐ Essie Summers 2   ☐ Rose Burghley
☐ Eleanor Farnes   ☐ Catherine Airlie   ☐ Elizabeth Hoy
☐ Susan Barrie   ☐ Sara Seale   ☐ Roumelia Lane
☐ Violet Winspear 1 ☐ Violet Winspear 2 ☐ Margaret Malcolm
☐ Isobel Chace   ☐ Rosalind Brett   ☐ Joyce Dingwell 2
☐ Joyce Dingwell 1   ☐ Kathryn Blair   ☐ Anne Durham
☐ Jane Arbor   ☐ Iris Danbury   ☐ Marjorie Norell

Please send me by return mail the books I have checked.
I am enclosing $1.95 for each book ordered.

Number of books ordered _____ @ $1.95 each = $ _____

Postage and Handling = .25

TOTAL $ _____

Name _____

Address _____

City _____

State/Prov. _____

Zip/Postal Code _____

PRAISE FOR *EXCHANGE ALLEY*

"Gritty and gripping . . . a fascinating read."
—**Wendy Wasserstein, author of**
An American Daughter

"Michael Walsh is an expert wordsmith and character-builder . . . and presents finely honed prose throughout."
—***West Coast Review of Books***

"Extraordinary and entertaining. . . . Dark, ominous, and tragic, this violent, vivid glimpse into the underworlds of New York and Moscow grips the reader and never lets go."
—**Tim Rice**

"Michael Walsh lurches the reader through the labyrinths of several underworlds, riveted by his whiplash style, confident that he will be there at the final 'No Exit' with his natural novelist's scalpel to reveal his characters, amazingly. Hang on!"
—**Gail Sheehy, author of *New Passages***

"Without pity or indulgence, Michael Walsh summons up the bent world of sexual and political corruption. The people in this arena are impossible to ignore. Enter EXCHANGE ALLEY and you will not be able to extricate yourself until the last paragraph."
—**Stefan Kanfer, former book editor of *TIME* magazine**

more . . .

"Complex, gritty ... well-written and
well-crafted. ... An impressive debut."
—**Milwaukee Journal**

"A darkly ingenious, disturbing story, told with
ruthless energy, scathing moral impartiality, and
bitter omniscience. Michael Walsh is at the start
of a brilliant new career."
—**Lance Morrow, author of *Heart: A Memoir***